M000188676

Almanac

perpetual

LADURÉE

Paris

Almanac

perpetual

LADURÉE
Paris

SCRIPTUM EDITIONS

This Almanac belongs to ...

_____

_____

HOME

Address _____

_____

_____

Telephone _____ Mobile _____

E-mail _____

WORK

Address _____

_____

_____

Telephone _____ Mobile _____

E-mail _____

Notes _____

_____

_____

_____

_____

january

1 january
New Year

_____

_____

_____

_____

2 january

_____

_____

_____

_____

_____

_____

A good heart makes a good character

3 january

_____

_____

_____

_____

_____

4 january

_____

_____

_____

_____

_____

The caprices of 'le jour de l'An'

Throughout French history, the official date for the start of the new year has varied wildly. In the sixth and seventh centuries, new year was on 1 March. In the Carolingian era, the year began with Christmas. Then, under the Capetian dynasty, from the twelfth century, it was decided that Easter should mark the start of the new year, which accordingly began on a different date every year. Finally, in 1564, Charles IX imposed 1 January as *le jour de l'An*.

ART DE VIVRE

Bring a little joy to others

Have you been showered with Christmas presents? And the children even more spoilt? Why not take some of the gifts you don't really need to a charity shop, or donate them to a charity that can pass them on to someone less fortunate? And, while you're at it, you could sort through your wardrobe, too (so creating all the space you'll need for any shopping sprees in the spring).

The ability to laugh out loud is proof of a great soul.

JEAN COCTEAU
(French writer and poet, 1889–1963)

Secrets of the fork

Forks are known to have existed as early as antiquity, in the form of metal hooks for removing food from cauldrons. They are believed to have made their first appearance on European tables in eleventh-century Venice. This followed the arrival in the city of Byzantine princess complete with her own two-pronged golden fork, which caused a sensation. Centuries were to elapse before the fork with four prongs made its appearance in France, bringing up the rear after the knife and the spoon. Lest we forget, Louis XIV ate with his fingers.

A generous man will himself be blessed.

5 january

---

6 january
Epiphany

---

7 january

---

8 january

---

9 january

_____

_____

_____

_____

_____

_____

10 january

_____

_____

_____

_____

_____

_____

_____

11 january

_____

_____

_____

_____

_____

_____

12 january

_____

_____

_____

_____

_____

_____

Chocolat Chaud

Hot chocolate

Serves 8
Preparation time:
10 minutes

1 litre fresh full-cream milk

150ml water

100g granulated or caster sugar

185g dark chocolate (min. 67% cocoa solids)

50g dark chocolate (min. 80% cocoa solids)

1. Place the milk, water and sugar in a saucepan and heat to boiling point. Meanwhile chop the chocolate finely.

2. Remove the milk mixture from the heat, add the chopped chocolate and mix with a hand whisk. Blend until smooth.

• Chef's tips •

If you like your hot chocolate thick, return the pan to the heat after adding the chocolate and heat to simmering point, whisking constantly to stop the liquid from catching. Remove from the heat and blend.

If the chocolate is too thick for your taste, simply add a little hot milk.

Once prepared, the mixture keeps well in a sealed container in the refrigerator for up to 2 days. Reheat in a bain-marie.

You can also enjoy the chocolate cold, in which case you can thin it slightly by adding 300ml of cold milk.

Mandarin or clementine?

Fragrant and juicy, both mandarins and clementines add a festive note to winter fruit bowls and brighten the dark days with their shades of gleaming orange – but can you tell the difference between them? Mandarins, originally from China, are full of pips. Clementines – named after Frère Clément, who created them by crossing mandarins with oranges – have none.

Some people think that you make a journey, when in fact it is the journey that makes or unmakes you.

NICOLAS BOUVIER
(Swiss writer and photographer, 1929–1998)

ART DE VIVRE

Le chocolat chaud

Marie-Anotinette had her own personal *chocolatier*, who prepared the royal hot chocolate using sugar and vanilla, orange flower water or sweet almond milk. The secret of hot chocolate lies in the quality of the cocoa. If you do not have the perfect ingredient to hand, you may have no alternative but to repair to a sumptuously decorated Parisian *salon de thé* – where divine hot chocolate will be only the start of your temptations …

13 january

_____
_____
_____
_____
_____
_____
_____

14 january

_____
_____
_____
_____
_____
_____
_____

15 january

_____
_____
_____
_____
_____
_____
_____

16 january

_____
_____
_____
_____
_____
_____
_____

17 january

18 january

19 january

20 january

*Some pursue happiness,
others create it.*

Vitamin Boost

To boost your immune system, always at its lowest in winter, cook wisely. Add sweet spices such as cinnamon and cloves to your shopping list, along with herbs such as oregano, thyme, savory and sage. And seasonal organic fruits and vegetables make delicious juices and smoothies that are packed with health and goodness.

Winter cheer

Even in winter, window boxes and pots can cheer windows and balconies with a touch of greenery. Heathers, dwarf conifers, evergreen shrubs such as euonymus and graceful bamboos all help to create the illusion of bringing nature into your living room. Ornamental cabbages, frilly and sumptuous in shades of pink, crimson, white and cream, add a welcome spot of decorative frivolity. Complete the picture with pots in complementary shades.

*For any meal,
no sauce
is more piquant
than hunger.*

CHRÉTIEN DE TROYES
(French poet, c.1135–c.1183)

Soft hands

Gloves may help to protect them, but your hands deserve some extra pampering once or twice a week. Plunge them into hot water to which you have added a couple of dessert spoons of honey, and give them a relaxing soak for 10 minutes or so. Then wash them with mild soap, pat them dry and massage them with moisturising cream or oil. Rosewater is another miracle product for soft hands.

A rose among thorns.

21 january

_____
_____
_____
_____
_____
_____

22 january

_____
_____
_____
_____
_____
_____

23 january

_____
_____
_____
_____
_____
_____

24 january

_____
_____
_____
_____
_____
_____

25 january
Burns Night

_____
_____
_____
_____
_____
_____
_____

26 january

_____
_____
_____
_____
_____
_____
_____

27 january

_____
_____
_____
_____
_____

28 january

_____
_____
_____
_____
_____

Beurre au chocolat et tartines grillées

Chocolate butter on toast

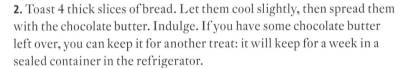

Makes 4 tartines
Preparation time:
15 minutes

200g butter
50g cocoa powder
1 pain de campagne,
or crusty loaf

1. Cut the butter into small pieces, then soften it in a bain-marie. Add the cocoa powder and mix.

2. Toast 4 thick slices of bread. Let them cool slightly, then spread them with the chocolate butter. Indulge. If you have some chocolate butter left over, you can keep it for another treat: it will keep for a week in a sealed container in the refrigerator.

· Variation ·

If you are a lover of milk chocolate, simply omit the cocoa powder and soften 50g of milk chocolate with 150g of butter.

Une table élégante

Embroidered, damask or plain, a white cloth is the perfect evening dress for your dining table. For a truly elegant dinner party, immaculate table linen – with matching linen napkins – is a must.

For special occasions a colour can also be a stylish choice: red or pink for a romantic dinner, black for a modern look, green for a spring celebration, or yellow for a summer spread.

DID YOU KNOW?

White as the driven snow

In modern Western cultures, white is associated with innocence, chastity and marriage, peace and spirituality. In many Eastern cultures, however, it is the colour of mourning. White is not a colour, but a value, sitting at the opposite extremity of the chromatic scale from black. It is both the absence of colour and the sum of all colours.

Man has the choice: to let the light in or to keep the shutters closed.

HENRY MILLER
(American writer, 1891–1980)

29 january

_____

_____

_____

_____

_____

_____

_____

30 january

_____

_____

_____

_____

_____

_____

_____

BEAUTY SECRET

LE SAVON NOIR

Black olive soap. Originally from
Syria, this wholly natural non-foaming
'soap' is a smooth, oil-rich facial and
body scrub made from crushed black
olives macerated in salt and potash.
Rich in vitamin E and sometimes
perfumed, it cleanses the skin to
leave it deliciously soft.

31 january

_____

_____

_____

_____

_____

_____

february

1 february

*Lovers of honey should have
no fear of bees.*

_____

_____

_____

_____

2 february

_____

_____

_____

_____

_____

_____

3 february

_____

_____

_____

_____

_____

_____

4 february

_____

_____

_____

_____

_____

_____

Candlemas

The Christian feast of Candlemas,
which takes place forty days after
Christmas, was first celebrated in
seventh-century Rome. Associated
with light, wealth and fertility, it
symbolises the purification of the
Virgin and the presentation of Jesus
at the Temple, and takes its name from
the candlelit procession that traditionally
formed part of the festivities. The *festa
candelarum*, or *la Chandeleur* in French,
subsequently became associated with
pancakes, their golden discs evoking the
sun and its return at the end of winter.
La Chandeleur is still celebrated in
France with delicious *crêpes*.

*Happiness
is unrepentant
pleasure.*

SOCRATES
*(Greek philosopher,
470–399 BC)*

À TABLE!

Cracking crêpes

Great chefs all agree: to make the
perfect pancake batter, you just need to
remember a few essential rules. Add the
milk slowly to keep the mixture smooth;
use equal parts of milk and water for a
delicate batter; if you think your batter
is too thick, resist the temptation to add
more milk, as this will make it stick
to the pan; and, last of all, add a dessert
spoon of oil or butter to the batter to
make it even silkier. As for flavourings,
vanilla, orange-flower water and orange
zest all make for irresistible *crêpes*.

Soupe, potage or velouté?

Do you know the difference between these great classics of French cuisine?
La soupe was the name given to the thick hunk of bread on which stew would be served in medieval times, and which soaked up the savoury juices.

Nowadays it means a hearty vegetable soup. A *potage* (from *potager*, meaning kitchen garden) was a lighter, more refined later introduction, sieved till smooth. And a *velouté* has cream added before serving to make it rich and velvety.

Great joys come from heaven;
small joys come from effort.

5 february

6 february

7 february

8 february

9 february

10 february

11 february

12 february

Un amour de bar mariné au pamplemousse
Sea bass marinated in pink grapefruit juice

Serves 2
Preparation time:
15 min

200g loin of line-caught sea bass

1 Thai green mango
1 stick green celery
5g fresh tarragon
1 pink grapefruit

30ml olive oil
5g parmesan flakes
1g unrefined sea salt
salt and ground white pepper

1. Cut the sea bass into 3mm dice and place in the refrigerator. Chop the mango flesh and celery stick into 3mm dice. Chop the tarragon finely and reserve.

2. Peel the grapefruit, slicing off all the pith. Remove the segments of flesh between the white membranes, collecting any juice. Place the flesh in the refrigerator. Sieve the juice into a small bowl and season with salt and pepper; mix together, then stir in the olive oil.

3. Tip the diced sea bass, mango and celery into a salad bowl. Season with salt and pepper and drizzle the grapefruit juice dressing over. Add the tarragon and mix.

4. Press this tartare mixture into a rectangular bottomless mould. Remove mould and dress with parmesan flakes, grapefruit flesh and sea salt.

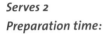

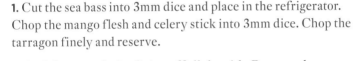

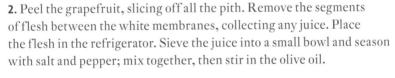

Valentine's Day

Although the many legends associated with the origins of Valentine's Day have little basis in historical fact, one thing is certain: today the feast of St Valentine is honoured in different ways by lovers the world over, from the Far East to Latin America. In Japan, it is the women who by tradition give chocolates to their beaux on Valentine's Day; elsewhere, this is the day for giving flowers: red for love, white for purity, pink for romantic tenderness.

À TABLE!

A MOVEABLE FEAST

For your Valentine's Day dinner, why not try something different? If you are dining at home, surprise your loved one by laying a small, intimate table in a different, unexpected setting or room. Dress it with your prettiest linen and your best china and glasses to create an elegant and sophisticated setting for a romantic *dîner à deux*.

> *Marriage is a very good thing, but I think it's a mistake to make a habit out of it.*

SOMERSET MAUGHAM
(British writer, 1874–1965)

13 february

_____

_____

_____

_____

_____

_____

_____

14 february
St Valentine's Day

_____

_____

_____

_____

_____

_____

_____

15 february

_____

_____

_____

_____

_____

_____

_____

16 february

_____

_____

_____

_____

_____

_____

_____

17 february

By swallowing evil words unsaid, no one has ever harmed his stomach.

_____

_____

_____

_____

18 february

_____

_____

_____

_____

_____

_____

19 february

_____

_____

_____

_____

_____

_____

20 february

_____

_____

_____

_____

_____

_____

WEDDING ANNIVERSARIES

The first wedding anniversary is traditionally cotton, the tenth tin, the twentieth china, the thirtieth pearl, and the fortieth ruby.
The fiftieth anniversary is golden, the sixtieth diamond, the seventieth platinum, the eightieth oak and the ninetieth stone. And if you reach your hundredth anniversary, you should celebrate it with water!

You must keep a few smiles in store for the gloomy days.

CHARLES TRENET
(French singer, 1913–2001)

Caring for your china

To keep a porcelain service at its best, always wash it in cold water. If you spot a little crack in the glaze, simply wipe it with a cotton bud dipped in hydrogen peroxide. Use lemon juice to remove any small marks or discolourations.

La fête du mimosa

In France,
February is the month *par excellence*
of mimosa, with its masses of tiny pompoms in
every shade from golden yellow and orange to white.
Indoors, its fluffy clusters of tiny blooms seem to glow
with sunlight, while they fill the room with their subtle
and highly distinctive fragrance. Mimosa is
traditionally a symbol of feminine energy and
security. To keep the blooms vibrant, change
their water daily; try slipping a frond of ivy
into the vase with them to keep
the water fresh.

21 february

_____
_____
_____
_____
_____
_____
_____

22 february

One joy will scatter a hundred sorrows.

_____
_____
_____
_____
_____

23 february

_____
_____
_____
_____
_____
_____

24 february

_____
_____
_____
_____
_____
_____

25 february

26 february

27 february

28 february

Blinis au tarama d'œufs de cabillaud et pétales de rose

Blinis with taramasalata and rose petals

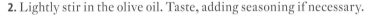

Serves 6	1 red rose with edible petals	12 blinis
Preparation time: 10 min	480g taramasalata	pinch fine salt
Cooking time: 6 min	2 dessert spoons virgin olive oil	pinch ground white pepper

1. Remove the petals from the rose and set aside 6 of the prettiest. Finely slice the remainder and tip them into a salad bowl with the taramasalata. Gently mix together.

2. Lightly stir in the olive oil. Taste, adding seasoning if necessary.

3. Divide the mixture between 6 ramekins or glasses. Heat the blinis in the oven until warm, then arrange them on 6 plates with the pots of taramasalata.

· Chef's tips ·

To add a touch of colour and freshness to this delicate hors d'oeuvre, *decorate each plate with one of the rose petals.*

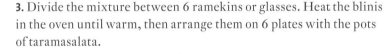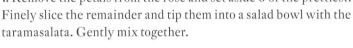

A gentle start to the day

For a relaxing start to the day, good lighting in your bathroom is essential. Ceiling spots give a pleasant level of general background light, to which you can add more lights to pick out specific areas. The most comfortable lighting for applying make-up should create a balanced effect that illuminates your face evenly: two of the best ways of achieving this are strips of ribbon lighting to either side of the mirror, or a mirror with bulbs incorporated all round the frame.

À TABLE!

THE CURIOUS KIWI FRUIT

Cultivation of the 'Chinese gooseberry', (as the kiwi fruit was originally known, after its country of origin) developed in the 1950s, not only in New Zealand but also in France, America, Italy and Japan. Its smooth flesh is our most concentrated source of vitamin C. If the fruit is yielding when you press it, the flesh will be soft and sweet; if it is still firm, the flesh will be sharper and more acidic. Kiwi fruits make the perfect start to the day: indulge in them to your heart's content at breakfast time.

There are certain shades of limelight that can wreck a girl's complexion.
AUDREY HEPBURN
(British Actress, 1929–93)

29 february

_____

_____

_____

_____

_____

_____

TIRED EYES

One simple gesture can bring rapid relief for tired eyes. Rub the palms of your hands together briskly until they start to feel warm. Close your eyes, and place the palms of your hands over them until the feeling of heat wears off. You can do this anywhere!

BEAUTY SECRET

A smooth complexion

Winter is hard on your skin. To soothe your complexion and lift the impurities from your skin, use a facial scrub once or twice a week. First cleanse your face, then apply the scrub gently with your fingertips, using small circular motions. Use the same facial scrub on your throat, where the skin is too delicate for a body scrub. Finally, moisturise well to leave your skin smooth and luminous.

march

1 march

St David's Day

The best mirror is the eye of a friend.

_____
_____
_____
_____

2 march

_____
_____
_____
_____
_____
_____

3 march

_____
_____
_____
_____
_____
_____

4 march

_____
_____
_____
_____
_____
_____

A nostalgia for violets

The days when florists and street sellers sold bunches of violets in spring are long gone. Since ancient times, this delicate flower has lent its sublime perfume to scents, refreshing colognes and deliciously fragranced candles. The scent of violets, subtle and sweet, takes us back to childhood and to a different age, to world of violet fancies and violet creams, candied violets and wafts of Parma violets around visiting aunts and grandmothers.

> *It takes a long time to become young.*
>
> **PABLO PICASSO**
> *(Spanish painter and sculptor, 1881–1973)*

A FRAGRANT HOME

For a natural fragrance that purifies the air, nothing can better traditional *papier d'Arménie*, or incense paper. You can also light subtly perfumed candles to create a warm, soothing ambience. Or try putting a few drops of essential oils on your light bulbs, so that when you switch them on the heat of the bulbs will fill the room with their perfume. For dinner parties, avoid any fragrances that are too heavy or invasive, opting instead for light, fruity or flowery notes. Empress Josephine, by contrast, was famous for saturating the atmosphere in her dressing room with musk …

Flowers good enough to eat

Pansies, wisteria and
mimosa have all been used in cooking for
centuries. And they are only some of the many flowers
that can be used to make delicious dishes. With their slight
pepperiness, nasturtium flowers make a delightful addition
to salads, while pretty blue borage offers a surprising
aftertaste of oyster. Dandelion flowers make excellent
jam, as do rose petals. Begonia flowers add a spicy
freshness to lettuce, while violets and lavender make
unusual flavourings for sorbets and macaroons. Some
flowers are poisonous, on the other hand, and to
be avoided all costs. Don't embark on any
experiments without consulting a
botanical field guide!

5 march

_____
_____
_____
_____
_____
_____
_____

6 march

To know that beauty exists ,
one only has to look.

_____
_____
_____
_____

7 march

_____
_____
_____
_____
_____
_____

8 march

_____
_____
_____
_____
_____
_____

9 march

10 march

11 march

12 march

Tapioca aux fruits secs

Tapioca with dried fruit

Serves 6

Preparation time:
30 minutes

Cooking time:
25 minutes

30g dried apricots
30g soft dried figs
1 carrot
1 onion
1 leek (green part only)
1 celery stick
2 litres mineral water
1 sprig of thyme

150g tapioca
30g sultanas
virgin olive oil
2 tsp fine salt
1 tsp *fleur de sel*
pinch ground white pepper

1. Dice the apricots and figs.

2. Prepare a vegetable stock. In a food processer, chop the carrot, onion, leek and celery stick. Pour the mineral water into a saucepan and add the chopped vegetables, sprig of thyme and 1 tsp of fine salt. Bring to the boil, skim off any froth and simmer for 15 minutes. Pass the stock through a fine sieve and reserve.

3. Cook the tapioca in the stock without letting it go completely soft (it should have a little 'bite'). Drain.

4. Mix the tapioca with the diced fruit and sultanas. Season with the remaining salt and pepper and drizzle over a little olive oil. Arrange in small dishes or ramekins, sprinkling them with a few crystals of *fleur de sel*.

Balinese finesse

If winter has left you with craving for pampering, indulge yourself with a delectable moment of relaxation in a bath worthy of the rituals of Bali. Run a hot bath, then sprinkle in milk powder, scented bath salts or almond oil. For a touch of sheer voluptuousness, strew the water with rose petals and bathe by candlelight, choosing scented candles that evoke the perfumes of spring.

DECORATION

CONSIDERED CURTAINS

In the living room, dining room or bedroom, curtains add the finishing touch to your interiors. Whether you are looking for something cosy and snug, light and airy or vivid and colourful, your choice of fabrics and shades can lend each room its own special ambience. The way you hang your curtains – using a rod with rings and hooks, a cable and clips, tie-backs or a pelmet – will also lend a different aesthetic to your decorations. And don't forget to give some thought to the acoustic effect you're looking for.

Wisdom is to have dreams that are big enough not to lose sight when we pursue them

OSCAR WILDE
(Irish writer, 1854–1900)

13 march

_____

_____

_____

_____

_____

_____

14 march

_____

_____

_____

_____

_____

_____

15 march

_____

_____

_____

_____

16 march

_____

_____

_____

_____

17 march
St Patrick's Day

*Better to light a candle
than curse the darkness.*

_____

_____

_____

_____

18 march

_____

_____

_____

_____

_____

_____

_____

19 march
St Joseph's Day

_____

_____

_____

_____

_____

_____

20 march

_____

_____

_____

_____

_____

_____

EYES SORE?

Too little sleep, too much stress or simple tiredness can all leave their mark on the delicate skin under our eyes. Nature has answers to the problem. Dab dark circles under your eyes with a mixture of olive oil and lemon juice, using your fingertips or cotton wool, and after a few days you will see an improvement. For any slight puffiness in the morning, a few ice cubes wrapped in a flannel, slices of raw potato or a cold tea compress (used tea bags left to cool are ideal) all work miracles.

No more tears

Your eyes and nose are streaming, your mascara is running down your cheeks and there is not a paper tissue to be found: chopping onions and shallots is no picnic. Peel them under a running tap, or put them in the freezer for quarter of an hour before chopping, and your problems will be over.

Life is like riding a bicycle.

To keep your balance

you must keep moving.

ALBERT EINSTEIN

(German physicist, 1879–1955)

Stuck with a label?

You just love that glass bottle and you have a new use in mind for it. But how to get the label off? All you need is a little patience. Brush any paper that won't come off with vegetable oil, wait a few minutes, then peel it off. If the glue proves the sticking point, soften it by soaking the bottle in hot water.

The heart of a perfect man is like a sea whose shores are so wide they are lost to sight.

21 march

_____

_____

_____

_____

_____

_____

22 march

_____

_____

_____

_____

_____

_____

23 march

_____

_____

_____

_____

_____

24 march

_____

_____

_____

_____

_____

25 march
Annunciation

_____
_____
_____
_____
_____
_____

26 march

_____
_____
_____
_____
_____
_____

27 march

_____
_____
_____
_____
_____
_____

28 march

_____
_____
_____
_____
_____
_____

Croustillants de chèvre au miel

Goat's cheese pastry parcels with honey

Serves 8

Preparation time:

20 minutes

Cooking time:

20 minutes

80g whole dried apricots

16 puff pastry circles of 11cm diameter

8 Saint-Marcellin cheeses

10g *fleur de sel*

1 egg yolk

100g wild honey

1. Wash the apricots and slice them in half horizontally. Place a pastry circle on a flat surface, and on it place one half of the dried apricot, followed by a Saint-Marcellin cheese, followed by the other half of the dried apricot. Sprinkle with *fleur de sel*. Brush the edge of the pastry circle lightly with egg yolk, place another circle on top and press firmly to seal the edges well. Repeat with the rest of the pastry circles.

2. Heat the oven to 180°C/Gas Mark 6. Brush the tops of the pastry parcels with egg yolk, taking care not to let it run over the edges, which would prevent the pastry from rising evenly. With the back of a knife, trace curves around 3mm deep from the centre to the edges, in the pattern of flower petals.

3. Place the parcels in the oven and bake for 20 minutes, until risen and golden. Serve them warm with honey. They are also delicious with a salad.

ATISHOO!

When the body is irritated by dust, pollen or animal hair, it unleashes its defences in order to prevent any foreign bodies from entering the airways. It is the brain that gives the order for these mechanisms to go into action. If – as sometimes happens – you want to sneeze but can't, looking at a bright light often prompts the sneeze reflex.

Pleasures are gathered, joys are plucked and happiness is cultivated.

SIDDARTHA GAUTAMA BUDDHA
(Philosopher and founder of Buddhism, c.536–c.480 BC)

DECORATION

Longer-lasting blooms

To make sure that beautiful bouquet lasts a little longer, first, cut the stems diagonally, remove any leaves below the water line, and avoid filling the vase to the brim. Add a few drops of bleach, a sugar lump or an aspirin to the water, and you will be surprised how much longer your arrangement goes on looking lovely.

29 march

_____

_____

_____

_____

_____

_____

30 march

_____

_____

_____

_____

_____

_____

31 march

_____

_____

_____

_____

_____

_____

À TABLE!

JAPANESE CABBAGE SALAD

That delicious salad of finely shredded
white cabbage that Japanese restaurants
serve, with a dressing of rice vinegar,
a few drops of sesame oil and sugar, is a
variation on an Asian recipe that is also
popular in Vietnam and Thailand.

april

1 april

April fools' day

Red sky at night,
shepherds' delight;
Red sky in the morning,
shepherds' warning.

_____

_____

_____

_____

2 april

_____

_____

_____

_____

_____

_____

3 april

_____

_____

_____

_____

_____

_____

4 april

_____

_____

_____

_____

_____

_____

GLITTERING GEMSTONES

They adorn your earrings, rings and necklaces. But what can you do when your precious stones seem to lose their sparkle? Simply immerse them in a little surgical spirit for a few minutes, then wipe them carefully with a soft cloth, finishing off with a chamois leather. Your jewels will be restored to their full splendour.

Everything has beauty, but not everyone sees it.

CONFUCIUS
(Chinese philosopher, 555–479 BC)

DECORATION

Spring colours

Spring is here. Time to ring the changes! And playing with the colours in different rooms can be such fun. Beyond your personal tastes, any strategy for interior decoration rests on optical illusion. Hot colours make the room look smaller and the atmosphere feel warmer. Yellows are stimulating, oranges invigorating, and reds bring vital energy. Among cool colours, greens are refreshing, blues soothing, and mauves and violets bring depth. Why not have some friends round to share ideas over a cup of coffee?

It is easier to get to know ten countries

than one man.

The origins of the sandwich

Of all the world's combinations of bread and fillings – hot dogs from Germany, hamburgers from America, kebabs from the Middle East, panini from Italy – one of the most popular is the sandwich, originally from Britain. It was John Montagu, Fourth Earl of Sandwich, who gave his name in the eighteenth century to this novel confection of meat held between two slices of bread. Too engrossed to leave the gaming table one night, the earl is reputed to have ordered a waiter to bring him roast beef between two slices of bread, so that he could carry on playing cards while eating his 'sandwich'.

5 april

6 april

7 april

8 april

9 april

10 april

11 april

12 april

Fingers au poulet, concombre et fromage frais

*Chicken finger sandwiches with cucumber
and fromage frais*

Serves 6
Preparation time:
20 minutes

150g cooked chicken breast

40g cucumber
5g fine salt
pinch freshly ground black pepper

50g fromage frais
200g white bread, cut in 5mm slices

1. Cut the chicken breast into slices 3mm thick. Peel the cucumber, slice it in half lengthways, remove the seeds and slice very thinly. Season the fromage frais with salt and pepper.

2. Spread half of the bread slices with the fromage frais. Add the slices of chicken and cucumber and cover with the remaining bread. Cut into rectangles of around 4.5 x 11cm and serve immediately.

· **Chef's tips** ·

If you want to prepare these finger sandwiches in advance, wrap them carefully in greaseproof paper.

SWEET ALMONDS

Is there anything sweet almonds can't do? Packed with vitamins and minerals, they also soften, comfort and soothe. Sweet almond oil moisturises intensely, nourishing your skin and making it soft and silky, and repairing the drying effects of wintry weather. Used as a hair mask, it gives tired hair a new gloss and shine. Sweet almond oil is also found in lotions, creams and soaps, and it suits all skin types. Nourishing, revitalising, versatile and easily absorbed, sweet almond oils and creams are an essential item in every make-up cabinet.

We must face reality with a touch of humour, otherwise we miss.

LAWRENCE DURRELL
(British novelist, 1912–1990)

TIP

Soft towels

What could be more sybaritic than stepping out of a relaxing bath or shower and wrapping yourself in a luxuriantly soft towel? To ensure softness, when you buy new towels, soak them overnight in water with a dash of white vinegar. Repeat this from time to time. Avoid using fabric softeners, which often have the opposite effect. Spin dryers, however, make towels beautifully soft.

13 april

_____

_____

_____

_____

_____

_____

14 april

_____

_____

_____

_____

_____

_____

15 april

_____

_____

_____

_____

_____

16 april

_____

_____

_____

_____

_____

17 april

Travel broadens the mind.

_____
_____
_____
_____
_____
_____

18 april

_____
_____
_____
_____
_____
_____
_____

19 april

_____
_____
_____
_____
_____
_____
_____

20 april

_____
_____
_____
_____
_____
_____
_____

Al dente vegetables

It's all a matter of taste, but most people nowadays prefer their vegetables cooked al dente, so that they offer a little resistance when you bite into them.

For perfect results, refresh your vegetables briefly in ice-cold water before steaming them.

The exotic mango

The luscious mango is a native of India, but its cultivation has now spread throughout the tropical world. Its many varieties all have smooth skins, shading from green through yellow, to orange and red, with irresistibly fragrant flesh that can be used in many different ways. Use it in salads with avocado and coriander, as a main course cooked *en papillote* with fish, or drizzled with mint syrup as a dessert.

There is no love sincerer than the love of food.

GEORGE BERNARD SHAW
(Irish writer and critic, 1856–1950)

BEAUTY SECRET

Play the movie star!

With the promise
of summer in the air, we yearn to
cast off our winter woollies and step into
something more glamorous. And what could be more
glamorous than vintage style? The most sophisticated
of today's lingerie, handbags, jewellery, hats and
dresses are all inspired by the stylish opulence of past
decades. Luxury fabrics – silks and satins, lace and
crêpe de Chine – are to the fore, while the charm of
yesterday's styles is adapted to contemporary
lifestyles. Opt for bohemian chic in timeless shades
from pastel pink to silver grey, and elegance,
sensuality and subtlety will become the
keynotes of your style.

21 april

_____

_____

_____

_____

_____

_____

22 april

Change your sky, and you will
change your stars.

_____

_____

_____

_____

23 april

St George's Day

_____

_____

_____

_____

_____

_____

24 april

_____

_____

_____

_____

_____

_____

25 april
ANZAC Day

_____
_____
_____
_____
_____
_____
_____

26 april

_____
_____
_____
_____
_____
_____
_____

27 april

_____
_____
_____
_____
_____
_____

28 april

_____
_____
_____
_____
_____
_____

Saumon fumé au citron caviar

Smoked salmon with lemon caviar

Serves 8
Preparation time:
15 minutes

800g sliced Scottish
smoked salmon

5 caviar lemons or
finger limes

8 slices white bread

1. Remove any dark flesh from the salmon and keep the fish chilled.

2. Cut the caviar lemons or finger limes in half lengthways and scoop out the caviar-like pulp.

3. Toast the bread slices.

4. Pile up the smoked salmon in a dish, sprinkle with the lemon caviar and serve accompanied by the toast.

· **Chef's tips** ·

The Australian finger lime, or caviar lemon, has flesh consisting of small pulpy vesicles that burst in the mouth with an acidic tang reminiscent of lemon with a hint of pink grapefruit. Use wholemeal or granary bread instead of white for this recipe if you prefer.

Sweet spears

Served with a light savoury *goûteuse* sauce, white asparagus has a deliciously sweet and delicate flavour that is one of the gourmet delicacies of spring. For the finest flavour, choose spears with pearly tips, firm, brittle stems and translucent white bases.

Experience is the name everyone gives to their mistakes.

OSCAR WILDE

(Irish writer, 1854–1900)

DECORATION

Adorable Anemones

The name of these beautiful flowers derives from the Greek word for 'wind'. In April they appear in florists' windows, in dazzling shades of blue, red, white and mauve that will brighten any room. Often they are sold in posies mixing all these colours, though single-colour bouquets are also very stylish. With their brilliant petals arranged like stars and their velvety black centre, anemones are highly graphic. They also last well when cut, either in bouquets or displayed singly. In summer they give way to their tall, slender cousins, Japanese anemones, in shades of pink and white.

29 april

_____

_____

_____

_____

_____

_____

30 april

_____

_____

_____

_____

_____

_____

ART DE VIVRE

UN CADEAU ORIGINAL

Have you ever thought of commissioning a portrait of yourself in your living room as a gift for a loved one, in emulation of the spirit of the Enlightenment? Choose a frame to complement it, and this original painting – whether in oils or watercolour, gouache or pastel – will make a highly personal, original and altogether different gift.

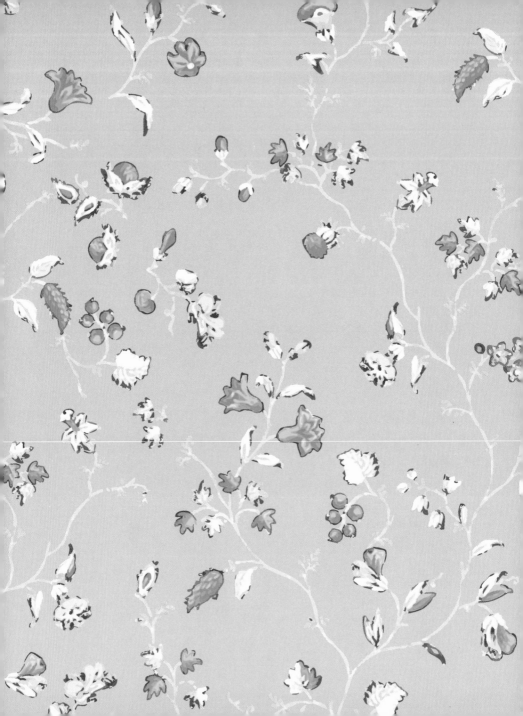

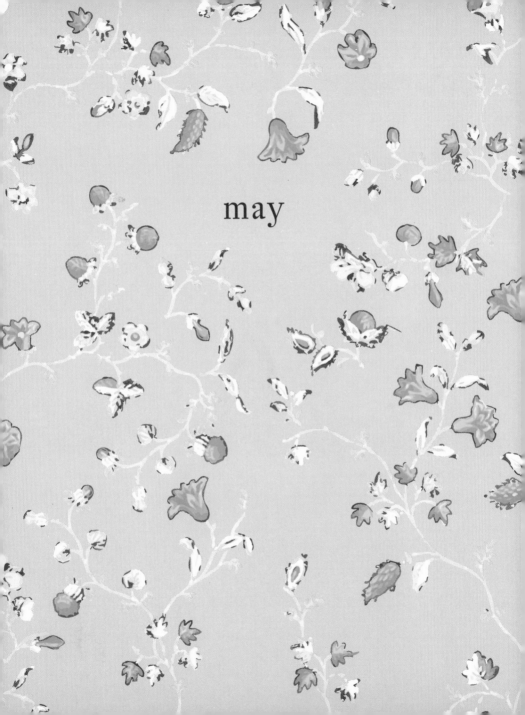

may

1 may
May Day

A good friend is cheaper than therapy.

_____

_____

_____

_____

_____

2 may

_____

_____

_____

_____

_____

_____

_____

3 may

_____

_____

_____

_____

_____

_____

4 may

_____

_____

_____

_____

_____

_____

Lily of the valley

The charming tiny bells of lily of the valley grow wild throughout the temperate regions of the northern hemisphere, and have for centuries been associated with May Day. In France the flowers are traditionally given for good luck on 1ˢᵗ May. Their musky fragrance has been used in perfumery since earliest times, and the flowers have held a special place in European mythology and culture for many centuries. Lily of the valley is the national flower of Finland.

ART DE VIVRE

Scents & Sensibility

We naturally crave fresh scents at this time of year, so this is a good moment to recycle any used perfume bottles. Simply remove the stopper and place the bottle in a wardrobe or drawer, where it will perfume your clothes. For an exquisitely scented linen cupboard, slip lavender sachets or bags between your sheets and towels.

Serenity is the secret of beauty and the real substance of all art

HERMANN HESSE
(German-Swiss writer, 1877–1962)

Sinful strawberries

Pick your strawberries – oval or slightly elongated in shape, flawlessly red with a perfect green ruff – for their glossy sheen and their fragrance. In May, this tempting fruit is at its peak, and, as they have virtually no calories, we can eat them to our hearts' content. There are so many way to enjoy them: in tiramisu, as a salad with basil, as kebabs with a lemon coulis, with rhubarb in a tart – the list goes on. If you are serving them simply as they are, grind a little black pepper over them a quarter of hour before they are to be enjoyed to bring out their full flavour.

Real discipline is when you can pick strawberries without eating any.

DOUG LARSON

(American journalist, born 1926)

5 may

_____
_____
_____
_____
_____
_____

6 may

_____
_____
_____
_____
_____
_____

7 may

_____
_____
_____
_____
_____
_____

8 may
VE Day

_____
_____
_____
_____
_____
_____

9 may

10 may

11 may

12 may

Soupe de fraises au vin rosé
Strawberry soup with rosé wine

Serves 4
Preparation time:
30 minutes
Cooking time:
5 minutes
Resting time: 2 hours

75cl Côtes-de-Provence rosé
150g caster sugar
1 vanilla pod
1 cinnamon stick

1. Put the wine, sugar, vanilla and cinnamon in a saucepan and bring to the boil. Remove from the heat and leave to infuse for 30 minutes. Sieve the soup, then place in the refrigerator for at least an hour (it should be served well chilled).

2. Gently rinse the strawberries, then hull them. Cut them in 4 or 6, according to size, and divide them between 4 small bowls.

3. Ladle the soup over the strawberries. Sprinkle with the freshly chopped mint and serve immediately.

· Variation ·

For children, make a syrup using grenadine and Bourbon vanilla. Dilute grenadine syrup in 7 times its volume of water. For each litre of the grenadine mixture, add a vanilla pod and allow to infuse. Chill well and ladle over the sliced strawberries.

Red, gold and black?

Each colour has its own special resonance and associations, and the colours used in a decorative scheme will affect our moods and feelings. Scholarly studies have even shown that the shades on a room's walls can influence not only the moods but also the conversations of those within it. A scheme based on red, gold and black will recall the splendours of the court of the Sun King, or the magnificence of imperial Russia: a simple way to create a sumptuous atmosphere for convivial entertaining.

Chairs with flair

If you feel your chairs are a little dull and ordinary, why not give them a lift by upholstering them in a new fabric? Taking your cue from the room's colour scheme, choose something light and bright, pretty and floral or shimmering and flamboyant. Find a good upholsterer and unleash your creative side!

I have decided to be happy, because it's good for my health.

VOLTAIRE
(French writer and philosopher, 1694–1778)

13 may

_____

_____

_____

_____

_____

_____

_____

14 may

_____

_____

_____

_____

_____

_____

_____

15 may

_____

_____

_____

_____

_____

16 may

_____

_____

_____

_____

_____

17 may

You cannot gild the sun,
nor silver the moon.

_____

_____

_____

_____

18 may

_____

_____

_____

_____

_____

_____

_____

19 may

_____

_____

_____

_____

_____

_____

20 may

_____

_____

_____

_____

_____

_____

Sumptuous soaps

Hand-made and artisan soaps are objects of beauty that will enhance any bathroom. Choose their shapes, colours and perfumes to suit your mood and your colour scheme. Cosmetic soaps with no chemical additives are kind to the skin and a delight to the senses. And the beautiful presentation boxes in which they are now sold also make them the perfect gift for any occasion.

À TABLE!

DARING SALADS

Be bold! Decorate your salads with strawberries or raspberries; try a combination of Parmesan, hazelnuts and fresh mint, a mixture of fresh coriander, sesame seeds and lime juice, or a marriage of pears, walnuts and Gorgonzola. Take your inspiration from the freshest produce in the market or shops and let your imagination run free.

Joy is like a river: it flows ceaselessly.

HENRY MILLER
(American writer, 1891–1980)

Exquisite screens

From its origins in China,
the screen rapidly spread to Japan and Korea,
where it became an indispensable feature of royal
courts and wealthy interiors. Over time, its wooden
panels were replaced by paper and silk, and
metamorphosed into veritable works of art. Available
in a vast choice of designs, decorated with floral motifs
or monochrome black-and-white patterns, in fabric,
reversible or made to measure, these small,
moveable partitions – as practical as they are
aesthetic add a touch of refinement
and charm to any interior.

21 may

22 may

A bird does not sing because it has an answer. It sings because it has a song.

23 may

24 may

25 may

_____
_____
_____
_____
_____
_____

26 may

_____
_____
_____
_____
_____
_____

27 may

_____
_____
_____
_____
_____
_____

28 may

_____
_____
_____
_____
_____
_____

Clafoutis aux cerises
Cherry clafoutis

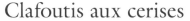

Serves 8	1 unwaxed lemon	3 whole eggs + 2 yolks
Preparation time:	175g caster sugar	300ml whole milk
15 minutes	+ 20g for the dish	300ml single cream
Cooking time:	1 pinch salt	500g cherries
40 minutes	50g cornflour	20g butter for the dish
	50g plain flour	

1. Preheat the oven to 170°C (Gas Mark 5/6). Use a grater to zest the lemon. In a mixing bowl, mix together the sugar and lemon zest, then add the salt, cornflour and flour. Add the whole eggs and the yolks and whisk. Finally, beat in the milk and cream.

2. Stone the cherries. Melt the butter, brush the inside of the dish with it and sprinkle with caster sugar. Arrange the cherries in the dish. Pour the batter over and bake for around 40 minutes, until risen and golden.

· Chef's tips ·

If you leave the cherries whole, your clafoutis will have more flavour and the cherries will produce less juice. In this case you can serve your clafoutis in a pate brisée (shortcrust pastry) case, pre-baked for around 20 minutes at 170°C (Gas Mark 5/6) until it is a very light golden colour. Fill this with the cherries and batter and continue cooking as above.

Moroccan miracle oil

Used before a shampoo, argan oil – made from the kernels of the Moroccan argan tree – will revitalise your hair and promote growth. Applied to your face at night or massaged regularly into your body, it will help to remedy any blemishes and imperfections in your skin. It soothes the skin after hair removal, and mixed with a little lemon juice it will improve your nails.

ART DE RECEVOIR

'Les petites assiettes dans les grandes'

If someone uses this expression (meaning literally 'putting small plates on top of large ones') of your host when you are in France, you know you are about to be treated to a gastronomic feast. It refers to the fact that plates of different sizes are reserved for different dishes. The largest (over 30cm in diameter) are for presentation only, and remain on the table until the cheese or dessert course, when they are removed. Dinner plates (approx. 25cm in diameter) are placed on top of them, and a smaller plate (but no more than one) may be placed on top of this.

Smooth runs the water where the brook is deep.

WILLIAM SHAKESPEARE
(British playwright and poet, 1564–1616)

29 may

30 may

31 may

ALIEN ARTEFACTS
IN YOUR KITCHEN?

Add a playful note to your kitchen
with a clutch of unlikely utensils:
a cutting-edge bottle-opener on the
fridge, an olive oil sprayer on the table,
servers in citrus colours, a pot of cocktail
mixers or – best of all – an electric
chocolate fondue-maker.

june

1 june

He who travels far knows much.

_____

_____

_____

_____

2 june

_____

_____

_____

_____

_____

3 june

_____

_____

_____

_____

_____

_____

4 june

_____

_____

_____

_____

_____

_____

Roses on your plate

Their fragrance, flavour and colour make rose petals a delicate addition to any dinner table. In exquisite shades ranging from palest pastel pink to rich raspberry and magenta, they add a graceful note to dishes ranging from *foie gras poêlée aux roses séchées* (sautéed foie gras with dried rose petals) and *poisson vapeur au beurre de rose* (steamed fish with rose butter) to bavarois ringed with rose-tinted macaroons or a delicate rose cream. Or simply use the petals and leaves as decoration (but don't eat the latter).

À TABLE!

LIFE IS JUST A BOWL OF CHERRIES

Who could forget the ripe, plump cherries of our childhood? The moment when you put the first bowl of glossy dark cherries on the table every year is ripe with anticipation and nostalgia. To stone cherries more easily, plunge them into iced water for an hour or so beforehand. Firm and juicy, cherries make a delicious accompaniment to poultry or sheep's cheese. But be warned, they are high in calories!

Wine is sunlight, held together by water.

GALILEO GALILEI
(Italian scholar, 1564–1642)

A little care & attention

Fabrics require different care according to their nature. Silk is extremely delicate and should be washed by hand in cold water. Never dry silk garments in direct sun, as this may bleach their colours. Linen can be machine-washed at a medium temperature. For white linen, avoid washing liquids and powders containing chlorine. Like silk, linen should not be dried either in direct sun or in a tumble dryer, as this could cause shrinkage. As for cashmere, wash it as little as possible! If you have to, preferably wash it by hand and keep it in the water for as short a time as possible.

Everything unknown appears magnificent.

5 june

_____

_____

_____

_____

_____

_____

6 june

_____

_____

_____

_____

_____

_____

7 june

_____

_____

_____

_____

_____

_____

8 june

_____

_____

_____

_____

_____

_____

9 june

_____
_____
_____
_____
_____
_____

10 june

_____
_____
_____
_____
_____
_____

11 june

_____
_____
_____
_____
_____
_____

12 june

_____
_____
_____
_____
_____
_____

Carpaccio de homard à la rose

Lobster carpaccio with rose petal julienne

Serves 2
Preparation time:
35 minutes

zest of 1 unwaxed orange

1 carrot

1 leek (green part only)

50g coarse salt

1 live lobster weighing around 400g

1 unwaxed lime

20g Parmesan

40g fresh ginger

1 rose petal

10ml olive oil

1 tsp *fleur de sel*

1. Place the orange zest, the carrot (peeled and sliced), the leek (roughly chopped) and the salt in a large saucepan. Fill the pan with water (leaving room for the lobster) and bring to the boil.

2. To prepare the lobster, place it in the freezer for a few minutes to dull its senses, then pierce it just behind the head with a sharp, heavy knife or skewer.

3. Wash the lobster and plunge it into the boiling water. Cook for 2–3 minutes, then remove.

4. To remove the meat, twist off the claws and legs. Break the claws into sections with a hammer. Tease out the leg meat with a pick. Next, split the body in half lengthways with a knife. Throw away the pale stomach sac, the gills, the green liver and the intestine.

5. Slice the lobster meat finely and arrange on 2 chilled plates. Sprinkle with lime juice and garnish with lime zest, Parmesan shavings, finely diced ginger and shredded rose petal. Drizzle with olive oil, sprinkle with *fleur de sel* and serve immediately.

COSSET THOSE FEET

Barely seeing the light of day throughout the winter, hardworking, unsung and suffering in silence, feet need as much looking after as hands, yet rarely receive the pampering they deserve. Naturally dry, the skin on your feet need regular care. Four simple measures will make all the difference: a regular soak in hot water with a few drops of your favourite essential oil; use a foot scrub while they are still damp, especially on your heels; smooth in moisturiser when they are dry; and, from time to time, treat them to a relaxing massage. In summer, remember to sprinkle a little talcum powder inside your shoes.

One must ask children and birds how cherries and strawberries taste.

JOHANN WOLFGANG VON GOETHE
(German writer and poet, 1749–1832)

BEAUTY SECRET

Prolonging nail polish

You adore the colour and it suits you perfectly – but then to your chagrin your favourite nail polish starts to dry up. To make it last a little longer, all you need to do is put it in the refrigerator. Then, every time you use it, add a drop of remover. But when it starts to go thick and gooey, you have to face the fact that its useful life is over. Always remember to protect your nails by painting them with a layer of colourless varnish before you apply your colour.

13 june

_____
_____
_____
_____
_____
_____

14 june

_____
_____
_____
_____
_____

15 june

_____
_____
_____
_____

16 june

_____
_____
_____
_____
_____

17 june

_____
_____
_____
_____
_____
_____
_____

18 june

_____
_____
_____
_____
_____
_____
_____

19 june

_____
_____
_____
_____
_____
_____
_____

20 june

_____
_____
_____
_____
_____
_____
_____

Pretty quails' eggs

Now the evenings are deliciously long, it's time for aperitifs on the terrace or balcony! Use your imagination to create tempting little amuse-bouches. Quails' eggs, tiny and speckled, make any occasion feel special and can be served in so many ways: sprinkled with poppy seeds and surrounded by wafer-thin smoked salmon, on a bed of salmon roe sprinkled with lemon juice, soft-boiled in their shells with miniature 'soldiers', or fried and sprinkled with truffle shavings.

NAPKIN KNOW-HOW

Napkins should be folded and placed to the left of the plate, or possibly on it, but never in the glass (a faux pas for the unwary). They should be used only for wiping the lips delicately before drinking. At the end of the meal, they should be left to the right of the plate; above all, you should never fold your napkin up again, which would be as good as saying, 'I assume I'll be invited again'.

Against boredom even gods struggle in vain.

FRIEDRICH WILHELM NIETZSCHE
(German Philosopher, 1844–1900)

Dye an old tablecloth

Bestow charm and
character on a boring old tablecloth or napkins
by dyeing them. It's so easy! Just follow the instructions
on a pack of fabric dye: usually you do it in the washing
machine, adding 500g of coarse salt. But remember that
dyeing won't cover any stains, and that some fabrics dye
more easily than others. If you want a paler colour,
reduce the amount of dye. Afterwards, try not to
expose any dyed items to the sun for too long,
as the colour may fade.

21 june

Summer Solstice

_____

_____

_____

_____

_____

_____

22 june

The moon wanes, the stars stay.

_____

_____

_____

_____

_____

23 june

_____

_____

_____

_____

_____

24 june

_____

_____

_____

_____

_____

25 june

_____
_____
_____
_____
_____
_____

26 june

_____
_____
_____
_____
_____
_____

27 june

_____
_____
_____
_____
_____
_____

28 june

_____
_____
_____
_____
_____
_____

Compote pommes-rhubarbe

Apple and rhubarb compote

Serves 5

Preparation time:
1 hour 15 minutes

Cooking time:
50 minutes

500g fresh rhubarb

375g Belle de Boskoop apples

75g butter

75g caster sugar

pinch ground cinnamon

1. Wash and trim the rhubarb and cut it into small pieces. Peel the apples, cut into quarters and remove the core.

2. Melt the butter in a large saucepan, then add the rhubarb and sprinkle the sugar over. Cook for 30 minutes over a low heat, stirring occasionally. Add the apples and mix. Cook over a low heat for a further 20 minutes. When the fruit is stewed, add a pinch of ground cinnamon. Divide between 5 small dishes or ramekins and serve warm or cold.

· **Chef's tips** ·

If you love strawberries, why not use them instead of apples? Add them to the rhubarb at the very end of the cooking time in order to keep their fresh spring-like flavour.

Put a cork in it!

To keep fruit in perfect condition, simply put two or three corks in the middle of your fruit bowl or basket. The secret? Cork absorbs the moisture given off by the fruit. In summer you can use the same method to keep tomatoes. Yet another reason to uncork that bottle of champagne!

BEAUTY SECRET

WONDER POWDER

Pure, simple, ecological and cheap, bicarbonate of soda has a surprising number of tricks up its sleeve. Added to shampoo, it makes hair silkier; mixed with toothpaste, it whitens the teeth; dissolved in your bath water, it softens the skin. If your feet are sore and aching, once again it will work miracles. And if you've run out of deodorant, it makes a better substitute than talcum powder.

Choose a star and keep your eyes fixed on it. It will lead you a great distance without exhaustion or effort.

ALEXANDRA DAVID-NÉEL
(French writer and explorer, 1868–1969)

29 june

_____

_____

_____

_____

_____

_____

30 june

_____

_____

_____

_____

_____

_____

Which lipstick?

Matte lipsticks give a creamy finish, shiny lipstick adds gloss and moisturises, pearl lipstick gives even coverage, and high gloss lipstick gives volume. When choosing a colour, take into account the colours of your clothes, as well as the shades of your eyes and hair and your skin tone. Test a little on the back of your hand, and go out of the shop to check the nuances of the shade in daylight. Whatever type of lipstick you choose, make it last longer by lightly powdering your lips before applying it.

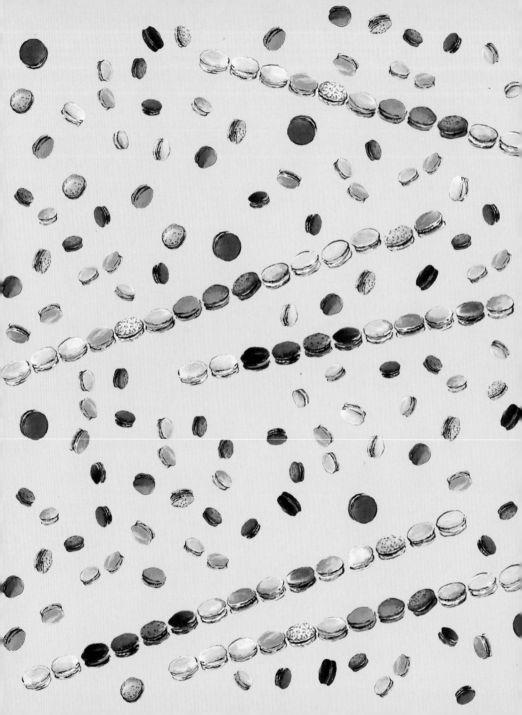

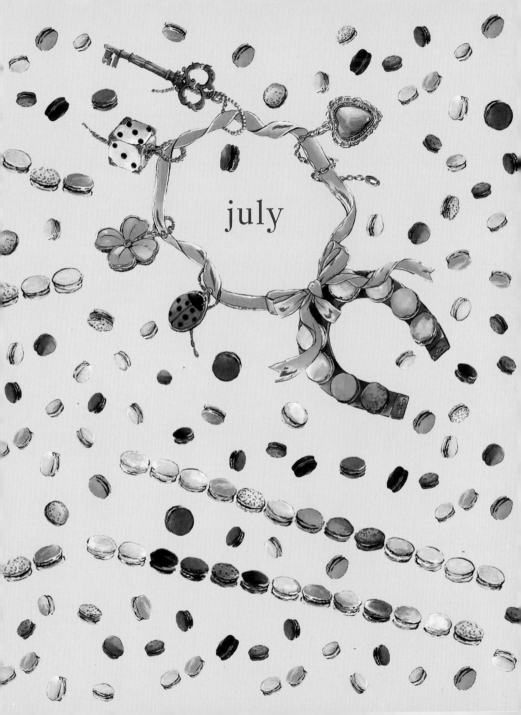

1 july

2 july

3 july

4 july
Independence Day (USA)

KEEPING MOSQUITOES AT BAY

The pleasures of dining alfresco on a balmy summer evening are all too often blighted by the attentions of mosquitoes and midges. Keep them at bay with mint, thyme and savoury – all fragrances that they detest. If one manages to bite you, rub your skin with garlic, a natural antiseptic that is also highly effective against wasp stings.

ART DE RECEVOIR

Déjeuner sur l'herbe

For a big picnic with lots of guests, nothing is more inviting than acres of white tablecloth spread out on the grass. Vintage linen or cotton sheets fit the bill perfectly, evoking the country tradition of spreading sheets out in meadows to dry in the sun. Or you could buy generous lengths of wide white cotton fabric – a cheap and practical way of creating a dramatic effect.

You can never cross the ocean unless you have the courage to lose sight of the shore.

CHRISTOPHER COLUMBUS
(Genoese navigator, 1451–1506)

Holiday packing

To avoid last-minute panics (and
the inevitable packing of things you really didn't
need), plan ahead. Shoes and anything else that is heavy
and unbreakable should go at the bottom of your bag. On top
of these go clothes such as trousers, jackets, dresses and
skirts: roll them up so that they take up less space and don't
crease. Then put in everything else in layers, with shirts
and blouses on top. Socks, tights and underwear can be
squashed into corners and any empty spaces. Divide
toiletries and make-up between sponge bags.
And don't forget a light folding bag for
bringing back your holiday purchases.

5 july

_____
_____
_____
_____
_____
_____

6 july

*To be for one day entirely at leisure is
to be for one day an immortal.*

_____
_____
_____

LADURÉE
PARIS

7 july

_____
_____
_____
_____
_____
_____

8 july

_____
_____
_____
_____
_____
_____

9 july

10 july

11 july

12 july

Oeufs d'oie mimosa

Goose eggs mimosa

Serves 6

Preparation time:
20 min

Cooking time:
12 min

3 goose eggs
10g fine salt
80g mayonnaise
80g crabmeat
10g parsley
2g white pepper

For the mayonnaise:
1 egg yolk
15g mustard
120ml olive oil
4g fine salt
pinch black pepper
1 tablespoon lemon juice (optional)

1. Place the eggs in a saucepan of cold salted water and bring to the boil. Lower the heat and continue cooking for 12 minutes. Remove the eggs from the pan and plunge them in cold water.

2. Make a mayonnaise using the ingredients above, or use bought mayonnaise, adding the lemon juice (if using) at the last minute.

3. Peel the cooled eggs, cut them in half lengthways and separate the whites from the yolks. In a shallow dish, crumble the yolks with a fork. Set aside half the crumbled yolks. Mix the rest with the mayonnaise and crabmeat. Add the finely chopped parsley and white pepper and mix well. Pile this mixture into the egg whites, then sprinkle them with the remaining crumbled yolks.

4. Arrange the eggs on a bed of mixed salad leaves and serve accompanied by toasted sourdough bread.

Perfect mayonnaise

Yellower, silkier and tastier by far than anything you can buy in a jar, homemade mayonnaise is impossible to beat. If only you could be sure it wouldn't curdle! First, keep the eggs and mustard at room temperature for an hour or so beforehand. Separate the egg yolks into a bowl, whisk them with the mustard and leave to stand for a few minutes. Whisk continuously with a small whisk or fork as you add a fine, continuous stream of vegetable oil. This is the key to the whole operation. To finish, add the juice of a lemon, which gives a more delicate flavour than vinegar.

BEAUTY SECRET

THE VIRTUOUS LEMON

In addition to its valuable role in cooking, the lemon possesses a whole range of other virtues. Lemon juice in the final rinsing water will give added shine to your hair. Add lemon juice to a bowl of water then soak your fingernails for a few minutes to strengthen them. Or squeeze it into a glass of warm water and drink it first thing every morning as an elixir for the complexion. Finally, add a few drops to your toothpaste to make your teeth even whiter!

To eat well in England you should have breakfast three times a day.

SOMERSET MAUGHAM
(British writer, 1874–1965)

13 july

_____
_____
_____
_____
_____
_____
_____

14 july
Bastille Day

_____
_____
_____
_____
_____
_____
_____

15 july
St Swithin's Day

_____
_____
_____
_____
_____
_____

16 july

_____
_____
_____
_____
_____
_____

17 july

_____
_____
_____
_____
_____
_____

18 july

_____
_____
_____
_____
_____
_____

19 july

_____
_____
_____
_____

20 july

_____
_____
_____
_____

Fabulous fruit bowls

Summer fruits are available in profusion now: why not turn them into a pretty display? Choose fruit that is unblemished and not too ripe. Start by arranging the largest, such as a pineapple or melon, in the bottom of your bowl or basket, then surround it with medium-sized fruit – peaches, nectarines and apricots.

Finally, dot your arrangement with small fruit such as strawberries and currants, tucking them into the gaps. For a special occasion, try an arrangement of exotic fruits, dried fruits or fruits of a single colour, adding some flowers for a sophisticated touch.

DECORATION

AN ORIGINAL AMBIENCE

How to create a festive but different setting, either inside or outside? Nothing could be simpler. Just fill a few pretty, medium-sized transparent dishes with water, then have a bit of fun with food colourings, adding a few drops of a different colour to each bowl. Finally, float tea lights on the surface and – for that special touch – a few flowers. The effect will be magical!

Patience is the key to contentment.

MOHAMMED
(Prophet of Islam, 570-632)

Laughter is the best medicine

Numerous studies have shown that laughter has the power to relieve pain, boost the immune system, ward off cardiovascular disease and reduce stress.

In fact laughter is both a muscular exercise and a breathing technique. And it's the best natural medicine there is.

My favourite pastime is watching the time pass, having time, taking time, wasting time, living out of time.

FRANÇOISE SAGAN

(French writer, 1935–2004)

21 july

_____

_____

_____

_____

_____

_____

22 july

_____

_____

_____

_____

_____

_____

23 july

_____

_____

_____

_____

_____

_____

24 july

_____

_____

_____

_____

_____

_____

25 july

_____
_____
_____
_____
_____
_____

26 july

_____
_____
_____
_____
_____
_____
_____

27 july

_____
_____
_____
_____
_____
_____

28 july

_____
_____
_____
_____
_____
_____

Crème glacée griottes et amande
Morello cherry and almond ice cream

Makes about 1.5 litres
Preparation time:
30 minutes
resting time:
3 hours
Equipment:
ice-cream maker

450g fresh Morello cherries

90ml whole milk

1.5l single cream

180g caster sugar

1 drop almond essence

1. Wash the cherries carefully, then stone them. Purée the cherries in a blender, then pour into a saucepan with the milk, cream and sugar.

2. Heat this mixture over a low heat until it reaches 85°C. As soon as the cream reaches a covering consistency, remove it from the heat and pour it into a large bowl to stop it from cooking any further. Continue stirring for 5 minutes to keep the cream smooth. Mix in the almond essence.

3. Pour the mixture into the ice-cream maker. Churn the mixture for 3 hours before serving in order to ensure the right sorbet consistency.

Versatile verrines

If you enjoy playing with colours, textures and flavours, verrines are made for you. Delight your guests with confections based on shades of green and pink, on smooth mousses and crunchy cubes, on mixtures of sweet and savoury, or any number of other tempting combinations. For a touch of surprise and exoticism, try marrying fish or vegetables with vanilla, ginger, star anise or cumin.

TIP

PEELING PEPPERS

A salad of red peppers makes a delicious starter. To peel the peppers, first grill them in the oven until the skin blackens. Take them out of the oven and put them straight into a plastic bag, then seal the bag. After about 20 minutes, the skin will peel off easily. Cut into strips and served with anchovies, red peppers also make a perfect aperitif.

Happiness is to continue to desire what one possesses.

ST AUGUSTIN
(Philosopher and theologian, 354–430)

29 july

_____
_____
_____
_____
_____
_____

30 july

_____
_____
_____
_____
_____
_____

31 july

_____
_____
_____
_____
_____
_____

DID YOU KNOW?

Growing in your sleep

The growth hormone is released during periods of deep sleep. This is one of the reasons why children tend to shoot up in summer: because they tend to get more exercise, they sleep longer and so grow more.

august

1 august
Lammas Day

_____

_____

_____

_____

_____

_____

_____

2 august

_____

_____

_____

_____

_____

_____

_____

3 august

_____

_____

_____

_____

_____

_____

4 august

_____

_____

_____

_____

_____

_____

Chaise-longue chic

The chaise-longue, or daybed, designed for ladies to enjoy a decorous siesta, is making a comeback. Whether classic or contemporary in style, upholstered in linen or leather or perhaps made of wicker, its long, elegant lines and slender eighteenth-century grace will add a rococo touch to any interior.

STAY HEALTHY

SAVOUR A SIESTA

Why not treat yourself to the luxury of a cat nap? Not just a pleasant interlude in a busy day, a siesta can also make up for a late night, as well as giving you added energy and focus and making you feel better and more alert. Even a five-minute doze is enough for you to feel the benefits; twenty minutes will recharge your batteries till the end of the day; and the supreme indulgence of an hour-long nap will bring you the full benefits of REM sleep.

> *It is not others who must change, but you.*
>
> SWAMI PRAJNANPAD
> *(Indian spiritual master, 1891–1974)*

Be kind to your hair

Sun, sea, sand and spray: the
things we love best about summer holidays all
add up to damaging cocktail for your hair. If it becomes
dry, brittle and impossible to manage, your hair is telling
you that – just like your skin – it needs a daily dose of
moisturiser. Be lavish with conditioning creams and lotions,
and opt for easy-to-use protective hair oils in spray, lotion
or liquid form. Once or twice a week, treat your hair to
a nourishing hair mask. Choose a brush with natural
bristles, and leave your hair to dry naturally.
Finally, a few drops of vinegar or lemon
juice in the final rinsing water
will give your hair added body
and shine.

5 august

_____

_____

_____

_____

_____

_____

_____

6 august

Happiness is a habit to be cultivated.

_____

_____

_____

_____

7 august

_____

_____

_____

_____

_____

_____

8 august

_____

_____

_____

_____

_____

_____

_____

9 august

_____

_____

_____

_____

_____

_____

10 august

_____

_____

_____

_____

_____

_____

11 august

_____

_____

_____

_____

_____

_____

12 august

The Glorious Twelfth

_____

_____

_____

_____

_____

_____

Salade Salanova et homards
aux graines de courge

Salanova lettuce with lobster and pumpkin seeds

———— • ————

Serves 6

Preparation time:

35 minutes

Cooking time:

3 minutes + 10 minutes

1.2kg lobster

250g Salanova or oak-leaf lettuce leaves

60g pumpkin seeds

5g fine salt

30ml white balsamic vinegar

2g ground white pepper

60ml olive oil

1. Cook and shell the lobsters (*see 9ᵗʰ June recipe*). Reserve the tails, elbows and claws.

2. Wash and spin the salad leaves; wrap them loosely in a damp cloth and set aside.

3. Spread the pumpkin seeds on a baking sheet and put in a pre-heated oven at 160°C (Gas Mark 5/6) for 7 minutes. Leave to cool.

4. In a bowl, dissolve the salt in the white balsamic vinegar, then add the pepper and mix in the olive oil.

5. In a salad bowl, arrange the salad leaves with the lobster meat. Scatter with the pumpkin seeds. Serve the vinaigrette in small dishes.

IN THE PINK

If you have turned pink in the sun, slices of ripe tomato will quickly soothe any burning. Compresses made from damp tea bags are also pleasantly refreshing on the skin.

A chic picnic

Tablecloth, silver cutlery, champagne glasses ... Have you though of everything? On the practical side, if you don't have a cool box an insulated bag will do just as well. Remember to put your bottles of water in the freezer beforehand. Finally, a bunch of fresh mint, or even better some citronella sticks, will perfume your picnic 'table' and keep the mosquitoes at bay.

The advantage of being intelligent is that you can always act like an imbecile, whereas the opposite is impossible.

WOODY ALLEN
(American film director, born 1935)

13 august

_____

_____

_____

_____

_____

_____

_____

14 august

_____

_____

_____

_____

_____

_____

_____

15 august

_____

_____

_____

_____

_____

_____

16 august

_____

_____

_____

_____

_____

_____

17 august

Where there is love,
there is light.

_____
_____
_____
_____

18 august

_____
_____
_____
_____
_____

19 august

_____
_____
_____
_____
_____

20 august

_____
_____
_____
_____
_____

Lissom legs

Hot summer days can often make your legs feel heavy. At the end of every shower remember to spray your legs and feet with cold water, and now and again soak your feet in cold water in which you have dissolved three aspirins. Walk as much as possible, especially after sitting or lying in the sun, and apply a refreshing foot gel daily.

The fan revival

With its old-fashioned, graceful charm, elegant and chic, the fan is back. A fully-fledged fashion accessory, ranging from sober restraint to ethereal transparency and from modest simplicity to outrageous exoticism, a fan should be chosen – like a hat or pashmina – to match your outfit.

When one has tasted watermelon he knows what the angels eat.

MARK TWAIN
(American writer, 1835–1910)

Caring for cosmetics

Beauty products should be
kept in a cool, dry place away from direct
light. During a heatwave, don't hesitate to put them
in the refrigerator. Any products that have been subjected
to extreme conditions should not be reused. Creams and
lotions are sensitive and should be looked after with care.
Cosmetics containing alcohol, by contrast (such as
hair lacquer, nail polish, deodorants and perfumes),
are less fragile. But even these don't last forever.
Trust your common sense: smell
and appearance are both
good indicators.

21 august

22 august

23 august

24 august

25 august

_____

_____

_____

_____

_____

_____

26 august

_____

_____

_____

_____

_____

27 august

_____

_____

_____

_____

_____

28 august

_____

_____

_____

_____

_____

Sorbet au mascarpone
Mascarpone sorbet

—————— • ——————

Makes 1 litre
Preparation time:
1 hour
Resting time:
3 hours
Equipment:
ice-cream maker

¹/2 unwaxed lemon
300ml water
200g caster sugar
220g mascarpone
50g fromage frais

1. Use a vegetable peeler to remove the zest, then press the lemon half to extract the juice.

2. Put the water, sugar and lemon zest into a saucepan and bring to the boil. Remove from the heat, cover and leave to infuse for 10 minutes. Sieve the syrup and leave to cool.

3. In a bowl, mix the mascarpone and fromage frais with the syrup, then add a tablespoon of lemon juice. Pour the mixture into an ice-cream maker. Churn for 3 hours before serving, in order to ensure the right sorbet consistency.

4. The sorbet will keep for several days if you decant it into an ice tray and put it in the freezer. Remove it from the freezer 10 minutes before serving to allow it to soften.

THE PERFECT EGG

To check how fresh your eggs are, plunge them in plenty of salted water. If they were laid that morning they will sink to the bottom. If they float, they are over five days old.

Banishing stains

Chocolate stains will vanish if you soak them in cold water. Terre de Sommières stain remover and talcum powder will both remove perfume stains from clothes. Lemon juice will bleach any brown spots on your hands. Drip milk onto stains on wool, then use cotton wool to absorb the excess moisture. To remove lipstick stains, rub the fabric gently with glycerin, then rinse. Even chewing gum on fabric can be beaten if you harden it with an ice cube and then quickly whip it off. And the magic solution for spilt wax? Scrape off what you can, then sandwich the fabric between two sheets of blotting paper and press with a hot iron.

Gastronomy is a profession of faith.

PAUL CARVEL
(Belgian writer and publisher, born 1964)

29 august

_____
_____
_____
_____
_____
_____
_____

30 august

_____
_____
_____
_____
_____
_____
_____

31 august

_____
_____
_____
_____
_____
_____

Water with a bucolic touch

Make a plain jug of water prettier and more interesting by adding a sprig of fresh mint, basil or lemon verbena. As a bonus, it will add a delicate nuance of flavour to your water.

september

1 september

_____
_____
_____
_____
_____
_____
_____

2 september

_____
_____
_____
_____
_____
_____
_____

3 september

_____
_____
_____
_____
_____
_____
_____

4 september

_____
_____
_____
_____
_____
_____
_____

Service à la russe

Russian service is the type of formal service most commonly used today. Unlike service *à la française*, in which all the dishes are placed on the table before the guests arrive, in service *à la russe*, introduced in the nineteenth century, dishes are brought to the table one after the other.

Good food and good wine, these are heaven on earth.

HENRI IV
(King of France, 1553–1610)

ART DE RECEVOIR

Guess who's coming to dinner?

Now is the perfect time to organise a dinner with old friends, or perhaps with new ones you've met over the summer. You're in the mood to be sociable and there's nothing you like more than a varied guest list – do make sure, all the same, that your guests have something in common, whether it be a work or leisure interest or perhaps living in the same area. Six is the ideal number round the table to ensure that the conversation keeps flowing. Finally, if both sexes are present, aim to balance them equally.

A chef in your kitchen

To keep that holiday spirit alive, treat yourself to a dinner at home with friends without lifting a finger! Open your kitchen to a chef who will concoct a delicious menu according to your wishes and your budget. This providential professional will arrive with baskets brimming over with fresh produce, and will then take care of everything. You, meanwhile, will have time to beautify yourself at leisure, before devoting yourself entirely to their guests. And – the cherry on the cake – the chef will leave your kitchen spotless!

The road to a friend's house

is never long.

5 september

6 september

7 september

8 september

9 september

10 september

11 september

12 september

Saumon mariné à la cardamome et menthe fraîche

Salmon marinated with cardamom and fresh mint

Serves 8
Preparation time:
20 minutes
Cooking time:
6 minutes
Resting time: 4 hours

8g green cardamom pods
15g fresh mint
800g organic salmon, skin removed

200ml olive oil
10g *fleur de sel*
60g lime

1. Place the cardamom pods on a baking sheet and roast them in the oven for 6 minutes at 160°C (Gas Mark 5/6). Leave to cool, then crush finely.

2. Remove the mint leaves from the stalks, then shred finely.

3. Place the salmon, cardamom and mint in a dish. Pour over the olive oil and leave to marinate in a cool place for 4 hours.

4. Drain the salmon (but don't rinse it), then slice it thinly. Arrange on plates and sprinkle with *fleur de sel* and lime juice.

· **Chef's tips** ·

Serve with blinis or toasted bread, plain or speciality.

ELECTRIC HAIR

Banish static electricity from your hair by putting some conditioner in one of your palms and rubbing your hands together until it is completely absorbed. Then run your hands through your hair for a couple of minutes and your problems will be over.

Every moment is a golden one for him who has the vision to recognise it as such.

HENRY MILLER
(American writer, 1891–1980)

ART DE VIVRE

The art of tisanes

To make a good infusion, put a teaspoonful of flowers or leaves per person into the pot. Verbena, lime-flower, star anise and thyme repay being left to infuse – but never for more than ten minutes, to avoid any bitterness. All these plants have a sedative, relaxing effect, and so are often drunk in the evening. Others, such as savory, ginseng and ginger, are more invigorating and are better drunk in the morning.

13 september

---

14 september

---

15 september

---

16 september

---

17 september

_____

_____

_____

_____

_____

_____

_____

18 september

_____

_____

_____

_____

_____

_____

_____

19 september

_____

_____

_____

_____

_____

20 september

_____

_____

_____

_____

_____

Egg on your face

To give your complexion an impromptu treat with guaranteed results, mix a few drops of lemon juice into an egg white. Leave on for 20 minutes, and it will feel just as good as any expensive bought mask. Wash it off with lots of warm water, apply some moisturiser, and your skin will be left feeling as smooth as a baby's bottom!

GOLDEN RULES

Stick to a few simple rules every day, and they will help keep you healthy with the minimum effort. Start the day with a large glass of water when you wake up in the morning; finish off your shower with a cold shower for your legs; spray your face with cold water before moisturising; use the stairs instead of the lift; avoid a heavy meal in the evening; and make sure you're tucked up in bed and asleep before midnight in order to get the full benefit of a healthy night's sleep.

If you are unable to find the truth right where you are, where else do you expect to find it?

EIHEI DOGEN
(Japanese Zen Buddhist master and philosopher, 1200–1253)

Well-heeled

For leather shoes, all you need
are beeswax polish and a soft cotton cloth.
For suede, use a clothes brush or a scrap of crêpe fabric.
To remove grease spots, apply Terre de Sommières stain
remover and leave for 48 hours. If they've been out in
the rain, soak up the excess water with a dry cloth.
If the damp marks persist, rub the shoes with half
a raw potato to absorb the humidity.
Use a conditioner regularly
to keep leather shoes
soft and supple.

21 september

_____

_____

_____

_____

_____

_____

22 september

*What is true by lamplight
is not always true by sunlight.*

JOSEPH JOUBERT

(French moralist, 1754–1824)

_____

_____

_____

23 september

_____

_____

_____

_____

_____

_____

_____

24 september

_____

_____

_____

_____

_____

_____

_____

25 september

_____
_____
_____
_____
_____
_____

26 september

_____
_____
_____
_____
_____
_____

27 september

_____
_____
_____
_____
_____

28 september

_____
_____
_____
_____
_____

Club-sandwich à la truffe d'automne
Truffle club sandwich

Serves 6
Preparation time:
30 minutes

6g fine salt
20g lemon juice
70g olive oil
90g celeriac
20g black truffle purée
300g cooked breast
of veal

100g black truffle
900g sliced white
bread
180g lettuce heart

1. To make the lemon dressing: in a bowl, dissolve the salt in the lemon juice, then whisk in the oil.

2. Grate the celeriac, dress with half the lemon dressing, then add the black truffle purée. Finely slice the veal breast. Toast the bread. Wash and shred the lettuce heart, then dress with the rest of the lemon dressing.

3. On a board, assemble the club sandwich: take one slice of toast and place on it a little lettuce, 2 slices of veal, a layer of truffle, a little grated celeriac, 2 slices of veal, a layer of truffle and a little salad, finishing off with another piece of toast. Repeat. Cut off the crusts and place the two sandwiches on top of each other.

TIP

CAVITY CONCEALER

You've just taken a picture down, and now you're left with a little hole in the wall. To fill it instantly, use a little white toothpaste. Perfect for a white wall, it can also be painted with a small brush when dry to match a wall of any colour.

There are two means of refuge from the miseries of life: music and cats.

ALBERT SCHWEITZER
(German-French physician and theologian, 1875–1965)

À TABLE!

Make room for mushrooms

One of the delights of late summer is the variety of mushrooms and fungi that appear in every French market, especially ceps, chanterelles, morels and boletus. These delicacies must be prepared with care. Above all, they must never be plunged in water, as this will ruin their flavour. A small brush is ideal for cleaning them. Cook them in a frying pan without any butter or oil, which they simply soak up. Cooked like this they will give up the water they contain, which you can then evaporate off over a higher heat. Then they will be ready for you to use according to your taste.

29 september

_____
_____
_____
_____
_____
_____
_____

30 september

_____
_____
_____
_____
_____
_____
_____

DID YOU KNOW?

THE PERFECT AVOCADO

To make an avocado ripen more quickly, put it in a bag with a banana, or roll it in newspaper. To make it keep longer, wrap it in aluminium foil and put it in the bottom of the refrigerator.

october

1 october

*The head may make
a longer journey than the heart,
but it will never travel as far.*

_____

_____

_____

_____

2 october

_____

_____

_____

_____

_____

_____

3 october

_____

_____

_____

_____

_____

_____

4 october

_____

_____

_____

_____

_____

_____

Keep that cracked crystal

A cracked crystal glass can always be mended or re-cut. If the stem is cracked the glass will be a little shorter but not noticeably so, especially if there are lots of other glasses on the table. Even if the bowl has been shattered beyond repair or the stem or foot is broken, don't throw the glass away. One day another in the set may suffer a similar fate. Then the two damaged glasses can be put together to make a single whole one. Since this is costly work that can only be carried out by an expert, it is only worth considering for glasses of value.

HEALTH-GIVING HONEY

Make sure you have honey in your store cupboard for the winter! A natural antiseptic, honey soothes sore throats and keeps them at bay. It also tones up your whole system and wards off those winter feelings of being run down and tired, making it a wonderful winter fuel and prophylactic combined. And why not also give yourself a pre-winter boost with a course of royal jelly?

Sleeping à deux makes the night less impenetrable.

MALCOLM DE CHAZAL
(Mauritian philosopher and poet, 1902–1981)

Le grand fromage

To compose a classic cheese board
you need at least five different cheeses, selected to
complement the rest of the meal. Aim for variety by
combining cheeses of different types: goats' cheeses, soft
cheeses such as Brie or Coulommiers, pressed cheeses such
as Beaufort or Cantal, and blue cheeses such as Roquefort
and fourme d'Ambert. Or you could choose different
varieties of the same type of cheese, or present a
gourmet tour of the cheeses of a particular region.
Alternatively, you could showcase a single
seasonal cheese, such as a creamy
Mont d'Or during autumn
or winter.

5 october

6 october

7 october

8 october

9 october

10 october

11 october

12 october

Omelette à la truffe

Truffle omelette

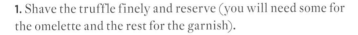

Serves 8	25g black Périgord truffle	80ml single cream
Preparation time:		15g unsalted butter
20 minutes	16 very fresh eggs	2g *fleur de sel*
Cooking time:	5g fine salt	
3 minutes	2 pinches ground white pepper	

1. Shave the truffle finely and reserve (you will need some for the omelette and the rest for the garnish).

2. Beat the eggs with the cream and season with salt and pepper. Melt the butter in a large non-stick frying pan, and when hot tip in the egg mixture. Using a silicone spatula, constantly pull the edges of the omelette back to the middle, so that the cooked part stays in the middle of the pan while the liquid mixture runs to the edges. After 30 seconds remove from the heat: the omelette is ready, even if the middle still seems soft and runny, as it will continue to cook in its own heat. Keep warm.

3. Scatter some of the truffle shavings over the middle of the omelette. Use the spatula to fold the omelette over, then divide into 8 wedges. Sprinkle with the *fleur de sel* and the remaining truffle shavings. Serve.

Bouquet de légumes

For something a little different, why not try your hand at composing bouquets that are not only decorative but also edible? Cauliflower and broccoli, artichokes and radishes, fennel and peas can all be used to dramatic, architectural effect. Mix round, billowing shapes with tall thin ones, and play with colour – arrange red and yellow cherry tomatoes on a green banana leaf, for example. For a purely decorative effect, arrange vegetables in transparent dishes or vases; for an edible arrangement, use a grapefruit or pineapple to provide your basic structure.

TIP

SPOTLESS KNIVES

When rust spots appear on a steel knife blade, you can remove them by rubbing them with half a potato or onion or a cork. If they come back (as they often do), very fine glass paper is effective; it may also scratch the steel, however, so should be used with great care. Polish the blade afterwards with *blanc d'Espagne* (*Bismuth Oxychloride*), or a gentle, domestic metal polish, applied with a soft cloth. Or you can adopt a more radical approach (though purists may be shocked): take your knives to a cutler and ask him to replace the steel blades with stainless steel ones.

13 october

_____
_____
_____
_____
_____
_____
_____

14 october

*Daytime is the father of work,
night-time the mother of thought.*

_____
_____
_____
_____

15 october

_____
_____
_____
_____
_____
_____

16 october

_____
_____
_____
_____
_____
_____

17 october

_____

_____

_____

_____

_____

_____

_____

18 october

_____

_____

_____

_____

_____

_____

_____

19 october

_____

_____

_____

_____

_____

_____

_____

20 october

_____

_____

_____

_____

_____

_____

_____

BLOW THE COBWEBS AWAY

Even when the thermometer is at its lowest, your living space needs a brief daily airing. Opening the windows for 10 minutes is enough to refresh the air indoors, so reducing damp and blowing germs and odours away.

Forgotten memories are not lost.

SIGMUND FREUD
(Austrian neurologist and psychiatrist, 1856–1939)

Fashion season

The high-profile 'fashion weeks' of autumn and spring are the pinnacle of the fashion year, when the designers of the great fashion houses present their latest creations to a waiting world. Key trends for the coming season are unveiled at a glittering succession of catwalk shows in the 'big four' fashion capitals of the world: New York, London, Milan and Paris (always in that order). Spring and summer collections are presented from September to November, and autumn and winter collections from January to April.

Craving cranberries

Cranberry juice, with its slightly sharp edge, is delicious mixed with orange juice. Dried cranberries make an original decoration for a cheese board or aperitif dish. Stewed slowly with sugar, they make cranberry sauce to accompany poultry or foie gras. Rich in vitamin C, this relative of the blueberry is appearing more and more often on our tables.

For the love of the rose, the gardener becomes the slave of a thousand thorns.

21 october

22 october

23 october

24 october

25 october

_____

_____

_____

_____

_____

_____

_____

26 october

_____

_____

_____

_____

_____

_____

_____

27 october

_____

_____

_____

_____

_____

_____

28 october

_____

_____

_____

_____

_____

_____

Baiser Ladurée salé
Savoury Ladurée kisses

Serves 6	7g sheet gelatin	10g fine salt
Preparation time:	5g fresh basil leaves	2g ground white pepper
20 minutes	5g chives	
Refrigeration time:	12g tomato powder	6 small savoury biscuits
12 hours	60g single cream	
Equipment: 6 moulds	600g fromage frais	12g black olive paste
in the shape of lips	70g currant tomatoes	6g *fleur de sel*

1. Put the gelatin in a bowl of water to soften. Chop the basil and chives very finely. Lightly dust the moulds with the tomato powder.

2. Warm the cream, then stir in the drained gelatin, fromage frais and currant tomatoes. Add the basil and chives, season, mix thoroughly and pour into the moulds. Put in the refrigerator and leave for at least 12 hours.

3. The following day, spread the savoury biscuits with olive paste. Unmould the tomato 'lips'. Sprinkle with *fleur de sel* and serve.

Odour-free hands

How to get rid of that smell of garlic from your fingers? With your fingers, gently (and carefully) rinse the blade of a knife in warm water. Do your hands have a lingering aroma of bleach? Rub them with water containing a few drops of vinegar. Mint toothpaste is also a highly effective way of ridding your fingers of unwanted smells!

The ideal of calm exists in a sitting cat.

JULES RENARD
(French writer, 1864–1910)

A MATTER OF TASTE

The sense of taste enables our tongues to distinguish five basic tastes: sweet, salty, sour, bitter and umami. While our taste buds deliver this information to our nervous system, our other senses – sight, touch and above all smell – also work hard to enable us to appreciate the flavours of food to the full.

29 october

_____

_____

_____

_____

_____

_____

_____

30 october

_____

_____

_____

_____

_____

_____

_____

31 october
All Hallows' Eve

_____

_____

_____

_____

_____

_____

november

1 november

Have the courage to follow your heart.

_____

_____

_____

_____

2 november

_____

_____

_____

_____

_____

_____

3 november

_____

_____

_____

_____

_____

_____

4 november

_____

_____

_____

_____

_____

_____

A good night's sleep

Every decade, we spend on average some 25,000 hours asleep – after which it might be time to think about changing the bedding! When it comes to bed bases, mattresses and pillows, there's no ideal standard: it's simply a matter of what's most comfortable for you.

Just keep two basic considerations in mind, whether you are looking for a single or double mattress or a base: choose the right sort of mattress for your physique, and opt for a firm and solid base, as this will act as a shock absorber.

BACK RELIEF

If you are suffering from backache, when you go to bed place two small, very soft foam balls under the painful spots on your spine. This should bring relief, so that soon you will be cradled in the arms of Morpheus.

> *I am persuaded that every time a man smiles – but much more so when he laughs – it adds something to this fragment of life.*
>
> LAURENCE STERNE
> *(Anglo-Irish writer, 1713–1768)*

The art of eating oysters

True oyster-lovers will
assure you that they are exquisite savoured
au naturel. You can also add a squeeze of lemon juice
or a little white pepper. In France, oysters may be graded
by a number indicating their size and in inverse proportion
to it (5 being the smallest). Oysters of medium size are
often the best. In the summer months they are milkier
and have less flavour than during the rest of the year.
All are at their best a few days after being removed
from the water. When you serve oysters don't
let them come into contact with ice, which
affects their flavour. A bed of seaweed
or coarse salt is ideal.

5 november

Guy Fawkes Night

_____
_____
_____
_____
_____
_____

6 november

A kiss is worth a thousand words.

_____
_____
_____
_____

7 november

_____
_____
_____
_____
_____
_____

8 november

_____
_____
_____
_____
_____
_____

9 november

10 november

11 november

Armistice Day

12 november

Coupe Ladurée

Ladurée sundae

Serves 8
Preparation time:
15 minutes

1l marron glacé ice cream

250g crème Chantilly

150g marrons glacés

1. Place 2 scoops of marron glacé ice cream in each serving dish.

2. Add a few pieces of roughly crushed marron glacé.

3. Pipe lashings of crème Chantilly over the top and scatter with more, finely chopped, marrons glacés.

GREEN TEA

It is calculated that, across the world, a billion cups of tea are drunk daily – mostly by women. Green tea is a friend to our bodies as it boosts our defences. To enjoy its benefits to the full, leave it to infuse for at least three minutes and drink it without milk or sugar. Just one caveat: green tea is not recommended for those suffering from iron deficiency.

Beauty is even harder to put into words than happiness.

SIMONE DE BEAUVOIR
(French writer, 1908–1986)

DID YOU KNOW?

Passion fruit potential

Originally from Brazil, this unusual fruit is high in beta carotene, potassium and fibre. The skin, which ranges in colour from purple to yellow, is wrinkled when the fruit is ripe. Other signs of ripeness are fragrance and heaviness.

Like kiwi fruit, it may be cut in half and eaten with a spoon. The pulp is delicious in sorbets and mousses. It also lends a subtle flavour to sauces to accompany fish. And it can be mixed with other fruit to make a vitamin-packed cocktail.

13 november

_____
_____
_____
_____
_____
_____
_____

14 november

_____
_____
_____
_____
_____
_____
_____

15 november

_____
_____
_____
_____
_____
_____

16 november

_____
_____
_____
_____
_____
_____

17 november

*A happy man is a small boat sailing
with a following wind.*

_____

_____

_____

_____

18 november

_____

_____

_____

_____

_____

_____

19 november

_____

_____

_____

_____

_____

_____

20 november

_____

_____

_____

_____

_____

_____

Boxing clever

Why not turn a gloomy Sunday afternoon into a spot of creative fun for all the family and brighten up those dull storage boxes? Use self-adhesive patterned paper in a variety of patterns – stripes or zigzags, dots or checks – to make your storage boxes more fun.

ART DE RECEVOIR

TABLE SERVICE

Soup should always be ladled into dishes laid on the table in advance. Every dish should be offered for second helpings, with the exception of the salad, cheese and fruit courses. To encourage your guests not to be shy, help yourself to seconds too.

To gaze at the river made of time and water. And recall that time itself is another river.

JORGE LUIS BORGES
(Argentine writer, 1899–1986)

Happiness is a ripe fruit just waiting to be plucked.

DID YOU KNOW?

Come rain or shine

First came the parasol, which, for the ancient Egyptian pharaohs, symbolised the vault of the heavens. For Louis XIV, parasols were decked with all the ribbons and laces that befitted the Sun King, while in Asian countries they offered protection from the monsoon rains. In 19th-century Europe, owning an umbrella signified that you did not possess a carriage, so many chose not to have one. Today, designers have turned this curious item into a fully-fledged fashion accessory, the very thing for brightening up a rainy day.

21 november

_____

_____

_____

_____

_____

_____

22 november

_____

_____

_____

_____

_____

_____

23 november

_____

_____

_____

_____

_____

24 november

_____

_____

_____

_____

_____

25 november

26 november

27 november

28 november

Cannellonis de saumon au chèvre frais
Salmon and fresh goats' cheese cannelloni

Serves 8
Preparation time:
25 min

300g fresh goats' cheese

60g unwaxed lime zest

20g chives + a little to garnish

5g *fleur de sel*

2g ground white pepper

600g smoked salmon slices

20ml olive oil

1. Put the goats' cheese, finely grated lime zest, chopped chives, *fleur de sel* and white pepper in a bowl. Mix together, then keep chilled.

2. Lay the smoked salmon slices out to form 8 rectangles, each on a sheet of plastic food wrap.

3. Place a spoonful of the goats' cheese mixture on one of the short sides. Using the wrap to help you, roll the salmon slice up in the shape of cannelloni. Continue with the other slices until you have 8 cannelloni. Alternatively, you can make larger rectangles and prepare longer cannelloni that you can cut into 10cm slices.

4. Garnish the cannelloni with chives and drizzle with olive oil. Serve chilled.

A relaxing massage

Are you feeling tense, tired or run down? Then it's time for a massage. Why not treat yourself to a massage in the comfort of your own home? Make a selection of your favourite essential oils (just like the ones used to pamper the wives of the pharaohs), then choose between the graceful movements of a Californian or Swedish massage, or the more energetic pressing and stretching of Thai massage. Whichever sort of massage you choose, you will be guaranteed a wonderfully relaxing experience.

DID YOU KNOW?

AN APPLE A DAY ...

The apples we eat today are the same as the fruit eaten by the Neolithic peoples of the central Asian plateau. Arriving along the Silk Route, apples quickly spread throughout Europe and now exist in hundreds of varieties. As they contain few calories they are ideal for snacking, and, as they are 85% water they are a valuable aid to hydration and to the elimination of toxins, especially after physical exertion. And to top it all, they are packed with vitamin C.

Great artists have no country.

ALFRED DE MUSSET
(French writer, 1810–1857)

29 november

_____

_____

_____

_____

_____

_____

_____

30 november
St Andrew's Day

_____

_____

_____

_____

_____

_____

_____

DECORATION

CREATIVELY HOOKED

Keys, hats, umbrellas, bags, pashminas, jackets … we've hardly set foot inside the door before we want to hang something up. And nothing could lend itself better to making your walls more personal and individual. Cast dull conformity to the winds and go for a mix-and-match approach, choosing different styles for each room. Available in a huge range of shapes, motifs and colours, unusual hooks and pegs are highly decorative and aesthetic in themselves.

december

1 december

It is darkest just before the dawn.

_____

_____

_____

_____

_____

2 december

3 december

4 december

Faux pas to avoid …

Putting salt on your food before you've tasted it; using bread to mop up the sauce on your plate; cutting salad up with a knife; not putting your knife and fork together when you've finished eating; putting a hand over your glass to decline an offer of more to drink; and leaving the table before being invited to do so!

TIP

NO SMOKE WITHOUT FIRE

For a crackling wood fire that doesn't smoke, the choice of wood is important. Choose chestnut, beech, oak or apple if you can – and make sure it is well-seasoned and dry.

Write it on your heart that every day is the best day in the year.

RALPH WALDO EMERSON
(American essayist and poet, 1803–1882)

DID YOU KNOW?

White chocolate

White chocolate is not really chocolate at all, and certainly not chocolate as the Mayan or Aztec civilisations would have known it! A derivative of chocolate, it is made from cocoa butter, sugar and milk solids. Cocoa butter is extracted from cocoa solids, but as it contains no cocoa solids it is technically not real chocolate. White chocolate was first developed in Switzerland in the 1930s as a way of using up a glut of cocoa butter. It is very popular with pastry chefs, who use it as a coating and for decoration.

To be loved, be lovable.

OVID

(Roman poet, 43 BC–17 AD)

5 december

6 december

7 december

8 december

9 december

10 december

11 december

12 december

Milkshake

Makes 1 milkshake
Preparation time:
5 minutes
Equipment: Blender

2 scoops vanilla ice cream

120ml whole milk

1. Take the ice cream out of the freezer 10 minutes in advance to allow it to soften.

2. Blend the ice cream with the milk, pour into the glass and serve at once.

· Variation ·

You can use any flavour of ice cream (coffee, chocolate, caramel etc.) to make a milkshake. If you use a fruit-flavoured ice cream such as strawberry, blend 50g of the fruit with the ice cream and milk.

· Chef's tips ·

If you pour the mixture into a deep receptacle such as a measuring jug, you can also use a hand blender for this recipe.

A WELL-SEASONED TEAPOT

A well-used teapot becomes seasoned over time. Tea connoisseurs maintain that this only improves the flavour, as long as you always use the same type of tea – the ideal is to have a different teapot for each sort of tea. If you want to clean your teapot without removing the seasoning, rub the inside with a little dampened sea salt.

In order to stop loving you I should have to stop living.

MARQUIS DE SADE
(French writer, 1740–1814)

Soothing lips and hands

If you suffer from chapped lips, try not to nibble at the dry skin, as this may make them worse. Use a soft natural-bristle toothbrush to remove any loose flakes every evening, before covering your lips generously with a moisturising lip balm. The simplest remedy for dry and chapped hands is natural glycerin: apply it thickly, leave it on as long as you can, then remove any excess by gently patting with a paper tissue.

13 december

_____
_____
_____
_____
_____
_____
_____

14 december

_____
_____
_____
_____
_____
_____

15 december

_____
_____
_____
_____
_____
_____
_____

16 december

_____
_____
_____
_____
_____
_____
_____

17 december

_____
_____
_____
_____
_____
_____
_____

18 december

_____
_____
_____
_____
_____
_____
_____

19 december

_____
_____
_____
_____
_____
_____

20 december

_____
_____
_____
_____
_____
_____

FOIE GRAS

A traditional Christmas delicacy in France is foie gras, preferably served with *pain de campagne*, or sourdough bread. The whole foie gras is chilled for a few hours, then sliced just before serving with a knife that has been run under a very hot tap, which makes it easier to slice evenly. About 50–70g per person is the usual serving.

DID YOU KNOW?

La crèche

French families who follow the tradition of setting up a little nativity scene or *crèche* at home do so on Advent Sunday (the fourth Sunday before Christmas). The most authentic figures in these complex miniature scenes are the *santons* (or 'little saints') of Provence. Historically they were fashioned from dried bread, then painted with oil paints and varnished – an art passed down through generations of *santon* makers.

No one is born under an unlucky star, but there are those who do not know how to read the skies.

TENZIN GYATSO
(14th Dalai Lama, born 1935)

Flûte ou coupe?

Aristocratic silver flutes
may have given way to smooth transparent
crystal, but champagne connoisseurs agree that
this glass – with its tall, narrow bowl designed to retain
those delicious bubbles and encourage the formation of a
delicate surface fizz – is the ideal shape for drinking
and appreciating champagne. With the coupe, on
the other hand, both bubbles and bouquet are
lost irrevocably. When washing your flutes
remember to rinse them well, as traces
of detergent will prevent the
bubbles from forming.

21 december
Winter Solstice

_____
_____
_____
_____
_____
_____

22 december

No road is long with good company.

_____
_____

23 december

_____
_____
_____
_____
_____

24 december
Christmas Eve

_____
_____
_____
_____
_____

25 december

Christmas Day

_____

_____

_____

_____

_____

_____

_____

26 december

Boxing Day

_____

_____

_____

_____

_____

_____

_____

27 december

_____

_____

_____

_____

_____

_____

28 december

_____

_____

_____

_____

_____

_____

Salade Salsola au saumon fumé bio
Organic smoked salmon with Salsola salad

Serves 6
Preparation time:
20 minutes

250g Salsola lettuce
20g shelled walnuts
4g fine salt
30ml balsamic vinegar of Modena

2g ground white pepper
60ml walnut oil
550g organic smoked salmon slices

1. Wash and spin the salad, then wrap it loosely in a damp cloth.

2. Spread the walnuts out on a baking sheet and toast for 7 minutes in an oven preheated to 160°C (Gas Mark 4). Leave to cool.

3. Make the vinaigrette. Dissolve the salt in the balsamic vinegar, add the pepper and gradually mix in the walnut oil.

4. Arrange the lettuce leaves in a salad bowl. Arrange the smoked salmon slices on a pretty serving dish and sprinkle with the toasted walnuts. Serve the vinaigrette separately in small bowls.

Flowers or champagne?

According to tradition, hostesses prefer to receive flowers from their guests rather than champagne, as they will already have a chilled bottle of bubbly ready in the refrigerator. But flowers mean that they have to go off and find a vase just as their other guests are arriving. The height of good manners, naturally, is to send flowers in advance.

On a roll

In France, where the perfect *baguette* reigns supreme, hostesses are beginning to appreciate the advantages – both gastronomic and aesthetic – of individual bread rolls. Rolls look decorative, and can be varied to suit different dishes: rye bread rolls are delicious with seafood; rolls containing figs or spices are delicious with foie gras; and walnut bread rolls are the perfect complement to cheese. Remember always to offer plain bread rolls as well, in case some of your guests prefer them.

Cookery has become an art, a noble science; cooks are gentlemen.

ROBERT BURTON
(English scholar and writer, 1577–1640)

29 december

_____

_____

_____

_____

_____

_____

_____

30 december

_____

_____

_____

_____

_____

_____

_____

31 december

New Year's Eve

_____

_____

_____

_____

_____

_____

Useful information & notes

Your websites

Address _____

Username _____

Password _____

Address _____

Username _____

Password _____

Address _____

Username _____

Password _____

Address _____

Username _____

Password _____

Address _____

Username _____

Password _____

Address _____

Username _____

Password _____

Address _____

Username _____

Password _____

Address _____

Username _____

Password _____

Address _____

Username _____

Password _____

Address _____

Username _____

Password _____

Dialling abroad ...

Prefix	Country	Country code	Area code	Time difference*
00	Algeria	213	Algiers 21	1
00	Argentina	54	Buenos Aires 11	-4
00	Armenia	374	Yerevan 1	3
00	Australia	61	Adelaide 2	8.5
			Brisbane 7	9
			Canberra 3	9
			Melbourne 3	9
			Perth 8	7
			Sydney 2	9
00	Austria	43	Vienna 1	1
00	Bahrain	973		3
00	Belgium	32	Brusells 2	1
00	Benin	229		1
00	Bosnia & Herzegovina	387	Sarajevo 57	1
00	Brazil	55	Brasilia 61	-4
			Rio de Janeiro 21	
00	Bulgaria	359	Sofia 2	2
00	Burkina Faso	226	Ouagadougou 30/38	-1
00	Cameroon	237		0
00	Canada	1	Montreal 438/514	-5
			Ottawa 613	
			Quebec 418	
			Toronto 416/647/905	
			Vancouver 250/604	-8
00	Central African Rep.	236		0
00	Chad	235	N'Djamena 51	0
00	Chile	56	Santiago 2	-5
00	China	86	Beijing 10	7
			Shangai 21	
00	Colombia	57	Bogota 1	-6
00	Congo	242	Brazzaville 28	0
00	Congo Dem. Rep. of	243	Kinshasa 1	0

Prefix	Country	Country code	Area code	Time difference*
00	Croatia	385	Zagreb 1	1
00	Cyprus	357	Nicosia 22	2
00	Czech Rep.	420	Prague 3	1
00	Denmark	45		1
00	Djibouti	253		2
00	Egypt	20	Cairo 2	1
00	Estonia	372	Tallinn 61/69/71	1
00	Finland	358	Helsinki 9	1
00	France	33		1
00	Gabon	241		1
00	Germany	49	Berlin 30	1
			Cologne 221	
			Dusseldorf 211	
			Frankfurt/Main 69	
			Hamburg 40	
			Hanover 511	
			Munich 89	
			Stuttgart 711	
00	Greece	30	Athens 21	1
00	Guinea (PRP)	224	Conakry 4	-i
00	Hong Kong	852		7
00	Hungary	36	Budapest 1	1
00	Iceland	354	Reykjavik 5	-1
00	India	91	New Delhi 11	3.5
00	Indonesia	62	Jakarta 21	6
00	Iran	98	Tehran 21	3.5
00	Ireland (Eire)	353	Dublin 1	0
00	Israel	972	Jerusalem 2	2
			Tel Aviv 3	
00	Italy	39	Milan 2	1
			Rome 6	
			Venice 41	
00	Ivory Coast	225	Yamoussoukro 30	-1
00	Japan	81	Tokyo 3	8
00	Kenya	254	Nairobi 20	2

Prefix	Country	Country code	Area code	Time difference*
00	Korea (South)	82	Séoul 2	8
00	Korea (North)	850	Pyongyang 2	8
00	Kosovo	381	Pristina 38	1
00	Kuwait	965		2
00	Latvia	371	Riga 7/28/29	2
00	Lebanon	961	Beirut 1	2
00	Libya	218	Tripoli 21	2
00	Lithuania	370	Vilnius 521	2
00	Luxembourg	352		1
00	Macedonia	389	Skopje 2	1
00	Madagascar	261	Antananarivo 22	2
00	Malaysia	60	Kuala Lumpur 3	7
00	Mali	223		-1
00	Malta	356		1
00	Monaco	377		1
00	Morocco	212	Casablanca 22	-1
			Marrakech 44	
			Rabat 37	
00	Mauritania	222		-1
00	Mexico	52	Mexico city 55	-6
00	Montenegro	382	Podgorica 81	1
00	Nepal	977	Kathmandu 1	5.5
00	Netherlands	31	Amsterdam 20	1
00	New Zealand	64	Auckland 9	11
			Wellington 4	
00	Niger	227		0
00	Nigeria	234	Abuja 9	0
00	Norway	47	Oslo 2	1
00	Pakistan	92	Islamabad 51	4
00	Peru	51	Lima 1	-5
00	Philippines	63	Manila 2	7
00	Poland	48	Warsaw 22	1
00	Portugal	351	Lisbon 21	0
00	Qatar	974		2
00	Romania	40	Bucharest 21	2
00	Russia	7	Moscow 495	3
00	Saudi Arabia	966	Riyadh 1	2
00	Senegal	221	Dakar 8	-1
00	Serbia	381	Belgrade 11	1
00	Singapore	65		7
00	Slovakia	421	Bratislava 2	1
00	Slovenia	386	Ljubljana 1	1
00	South Africa	27	Pretoria 12	1

Prefix	Country	Country code	Area code	Time difference*
00	Spain	34	Barcelona 93	1
			Madrid 91	
00	Sweden	46	Gothenburg 31	1
			Stockholm 8	
00	Switzerland	41	Berne 31	1
			Geneva 22	
			Zurich 43/44	
00	Syria	963	Damascus 11	2
00	Taiwan	886	Taipei 2	7
00	Thailand	66	Bangkok 2	6
00	Togo	228	Lomé 2	-1
00	Tunisia	216	Tunis 1	0
00	Turkey	90	Ankara 312	2
			Istanbul 212/216	
00	Ukraine	380		2
00	United Arab Emirates	971	Abu Dhabi 2	3
00	United States of America	1	Atlanta 404/678/770	-5
			Boston 617/781	-5
			Chicago 224/312 331/630/773/847	-6
			Honolulu 808	-11
			Los Angeles 213/310 323/424/562/626	-8
			Miami 305/786	-5
			New York 212/347 646/718/917	-5
			San Francisco 415	-8
			Washington, D.C. 202	-5
00	Uruguay	598	Montevideo 2	-4
00	Venezuela	58	Caracas 212	-5
00	Vietnam	84	Hanoi 4	6
00	Zimbabwe	263	Harare 4	1

*Time differences will vary throughout the year, as different countries osbserve DST at different times, if at all.

Conversion tables

LENGTH

1 inch (in) = 2.54 centimetres
1 foot (ft) = 30.48 centimetres
1 yard (yd) = 0.9144 metre
1 mile (ml) = 1.6093 kilometres
1 kilometre (km) = 0.6214 mile
1 nautical mile (in) = 1.852 kilometres

WEIGHT

1 ounce (oz) = 28.3495 grams
(UK) 1 pound (lb) = 0.4536 kilograms
(US) 1 short ton (tn) = 0.9072 tonne
(UK) 1 long ton (tn) = 1.0160 tonnes
1 hundredweight (US) (cwt) = 45.36 kilograms
1 hundredweight (UK) (cwt) = 50.80 kilograms

AREA

1 square inch (sq.in) = 6.4516cm^2
1 square foot (sq.ft) = 929.03cm^2
1 square yard (sq.yd) = 0.8361m^2
1 square mile (sq.ml) = 2.590km^2

TEMPERATURE

To convert °C to °F, multiply by 1.8 and add 32
To convert °F to °C, subtract 32 and multiply by 0.55

°C	-25	-20	-15	-10	-5	0	5	10	15	20	25	30	35
°F	-13	-4	5	14	23	32	41	50	59	68	77	86	95

VOLUME

1 cubic foot (cu.ft) = 28.317cm³
1 cubic yard (cu.yd) = 0.7646m³
1 ounce (US) (fl oz) = 0.0296 litre
1 ounce (UK) (fl oz) = 0.0284 litre
1 quart (US) (qt) = 0.9463 litre
1 quart (UK) (qt) = 1.1365 litres
1 gallon (US) (gal) = 3.7853 litres
1 gallon (UK) (gal) = 4.5460 litres

CLOTHING SIZES

| WOMEN | | | | | | | | | MEN | | | | | | | | |
| CLOTHES | | | | SHOES | | | | | CLOTHES | | | | SHOES | | | | |
E	GB	US	J	E	I	GB	US	J	E	GB	US	J	E	I	GB	US	J
34	6	4	-	34	33	1	3½	22	44	34	34	88	39	38	5	6½	24½
36	8	6	7	35	34	2	4	22½	46	36	36	92	40	39	6	7	25
38	10	8	9	36	35	3	5	23	48	38	38	96	41	40	7	8	25½
40	12	10	11	37	36	4	6	23½	50	40	40	100	42	41	8	9	26
42	14	12	13	38	37	5	6½	24	52	42	42	104	43	42	9	10	26½
44	16	14	15	39	38	6	7½	24½	54	44	44	108	44	43	9½	10½	27
46	18	16	-	40	39	7	8	25	56	46	46	112	45	44	10½	11½	27½
48	20	18	-	41	40	8	9	25½	58	48	48	116	46	45	11	12	28

Maisons Ladurée
around the world

UK

Ladurée Cornhill
14 Cornhill
London EC3V 3ND
Tel : +44 (0)207 283 5727

Ladurée at Harrods
87/135 Brompton Road
London SW1X 7XL
Tel : +44 (0)203 155 0111
Fax : +44 (0)203 155 0112

Ladurée Burlington Arcade
71-72 Burlington Arcade
London W1J 0QX
Tel : +44 (0)207 491 9155

Ladurée Covent Garden
1 The Market Covent Garden
London WC2E 8RA
Tel : +44 (0)207 240 0706

FRANCE

Ladurée Bonaparte
21, rue Bonaparte - 75006 Paris
Tel : +33 (0)1 44 07 64 87
Fax : +33 (0)1 44 07 64 93

Ladurée Royale
16-18, rue Royale - 75008 Paris
Tel : +33 (0)1 42 60 21 79
Fax : +33 (0)1 49 27 01 95

Ladurée Champs-Élysées
75, avenue des Champs-Élysées
75008 Paris
Tel : +33 (0)1 40 75 08 75
Fax : +33 (0)1 40 75 06 75

Printemps de la Mode Haussmann
64, boulevard Haussmann
75009 Paris
Tel : +33 (0)1 42 82 40 10
Fax : +33 (0)1 42 82 62 00

Printemps de la Maison Haussmann

64, boulevard Haussmann
75009 Paris
Tel : +33 (0)1 42 82 40 10
Fax : +33 (0)1 42 82 62 00

Ladurée Versailles

Château de Versailles
78 000 Versailles
Tel : +33 (0)1 30 83 04 02

Ladurée Aéroport Paris Orly

Carrosse Orly
Terminal Orly Ouest
Zone Publique Niveau Départ Hall 2
Tel : +33 (0)1 70 03 70 44

Terminal Orly Ouest
Zone Publique Niveau Départ Hall 2
Tel : +33 (0)1 74 22 07 77

Ladurée Aéroport Roissy-Charles de Gaulle

Terminaux 2F1, 2F2, 2E zone sous douane
et 2E zone publique
Tel : +33 (0)1 48 62 06 49

Ladurée Roissy AC

Zone commerciale sous douane
Terminal AC
Tel : +33 (0)1 74 25 42 45
Fax : +33 (0)1 74 37 12 92

REST OF THE WORLD

Ladurée Monaco

Galerie Métrople
17, avenue des Spélugues, Monaco
Tel : +377 97 98 42 96

Ladurée Genève

7, cours de Rive
1204 Geneva, Switzerland
Tel : +41 (0)22 310 44 04
Fax : +41 (0)22 310 44 05

Ladurée Bon Génie

34, rue du Marché
1204 Geneva, Switzerland

Ladurée Lausanne

Rue du Bourg 3
1003 Lausanne, Switzerland
Tel : +41 (0)21 312 7900

Ladurée Zurich

17 Kuttelgasse
8001 Zurich, Switzerland
Tel: +41 (0)44 211 88 84

Ladurée Luxembourg

18, rue Philippe II
2340 Luxembourg
Tel: +352 24 61 85 29

Ladurée Dublin

Ladurée at Brown - Thomas
88/95 Grafton Street
Dublin, Eire
Tel: +353 1 605 6666 (ext: 1606)

Ladurée Milan

Via Spadari, 6
20123 Milan, Italy
Tel: +39 (0)2 87 61 49

Ladurée Milan chez Excelsior

Galleria del Corso nr 4
Milan, Italy
Tel: 02/76281394

Ladurée Stockholm

Grev Turegatan 15
114 46 Stockholm, Sweden
Tel: +46 (0)8 660 40 50

Ladurée New York

864 Madison Avenue
New York 10021, USA
Tel: +1 646 558 3157

Ladurée Shinjuku

Shinjuku Lumine 2, 1F
3-38-2 Shinjuku-ku, Shinjuku
Tokyo, 160-0022, Japan
Tel: +81 (0)3 6380 5981
Fax: +81 (0)3 6380 5982

Ladurée Ginza Mitsukoshi

Ginza Mitsukoshi 2F
4-6-16, Ginza Chuo-ku
Tokyo 104-8212, Japan
Tel: +81 (0)3 3563 2120

Ladurée chez Nihombashi Mitsukoshi

Mitsukoshi Honten Honkan B1F
1-4-1, Nihonbashi Muromachi, Chuo-ku
Tokyo 103-8001, Japan
Tel: +81 (0)3 3274 0355

Ladurée Nagoya

JR Nagoya Takashimaya 2F
1-1-4, Mei-Eki, Nakamura-ku, Nagoya-shi
Nagoya 450-6001, Japan
Tel: +81 (0)52 566 3877

Ladurée Shinsaibashi

Daimaru Shinsaibashi North Bld 1F
1-7-1, Shinsaibashisuji, Chuo-ku, Osaka-shi
Osaka 542-8501, Japan
Tel : +81 (0)66 125 5830

Ladurée Osaka

JR Osaka Mitsukoshi Isetan 2F
3-1-3, Umeda, Kita-ku, Osaka-shi
Osaka 530-8558, Japan
Tel : +81 (0)66 485 7588

Ladurée Beyrouth

128, rue Foch
Beirut, Libya
Tel : +961 01 992 922
Fax : +961 70 992 922

Ladurée Istanbul

Cevdet Pasa caddesi 63/A Bebek
34342 Istanbul, Turkey
Tel : +90 (0)212 263 57 42

Ladurée Istinye Park

Istinye Park
Istanbul, Turkey
Tel : +90 (0)212 345 54 20 / 21

Ladurée Riyad

Luxury Sweet Co. Centria Mall 2nd floor
Olaya Street, PO Box 88942
11672 Riyadh, Kingdom of Saudi Arabia
Tel : +966 288 5075
M : +966 5555 46 888
(Arabic & English Speaking)
Fax : +966 288 5071

Ladurée Dubaï

French Spirit Coffee Shop 1st Floor
The Dubaï Mall
B.P. 112434 Dubaï, UAE
Tel : +971 4 33 98 520
Fax : +971 4 33 98 904

Ladurée Koweit

French Food Company Laduree 360 Mall
6 Ring Road, 71955 Al Zahraa, Kuwait
Tel : +965 25 30 96 68
Fax : +965 25 30 96 65

Ladurée Qatar

VIP SECTION – Villagio Mall
Doha, Qatar
Tel : 00974 444 74 001

NOTES

NOTES

NOTES

NOTES

NOTES

NOTES

TEXT

Zahia Hafs

SWEET RECIPES

Vincent Lemains, *Chef pâtissier*

SAVOURY RECIPES

Michel Lerouet, *Chef de cuisine*

Editorial Manager: *Valérie Tognali*

Editorial Assistant: *Françoise Mathay*

Artistic Director: *Sabine Houplain*
assisted by *Marion Rosière* & *Audrey Lorel*

Graphic Design: *Marie-Paule Jaulme*

Translation: *Barbara Mellor*

Publishers: *Beatrice Vincenzini* & *Francesco Venturi*

Published in the UK by Scriptum Editions, 2012

An imprint of Co & Bear Productions (UK) Ltd

63 Edith Grove, London, SW10 0LB

www.scriptumeditions.co.uk

First published in French by
Editions du Chêne – Hachette Livre, 2012

Original title: *L'Almanach perpétuel - Ladurée - Paris*

© 2012 for Editions du Chêne

Translation © Co & Bear Productions (UK) Ltd, 2012

Distributed by Thames & Hudson

2 4 6 8 10 9 7 5 3 1

ISBN: 978–1–902686–78–3

*All rights reserved. No part of this book may be reproduced in any form,
or by any means without permission in writing from the copyright holder.*